DATE DUE

SCRIPPS INSTITUTION OF OCEANOGRAPHY

SCRIPPS

INSTITUTION

OF OCEANOGRAPHY

FIRST FIFTY YEARS

BY HELEN RAITT
AND BEATRICE MOULTON

The Ward Ritchie Press

TO

ROGER R. REVELLE

WHO SAID IN A CHARTER DAY ADDRESS

MARCH 22, 1950

"But a university is not great because it has many hundreds of buildings, thousands of employees, tens of thousands of students or millions of dollars of annual income. A university is not great because it has elegant classrooms, laboratories full of equipment, a well stocked library, a business-like administration or a winning football team.

Like all human institutions, a university is the product of the work and devotion of individual men and women, and it can be great only in so far as it can obtain the fullest measure of creative accomplishment from the men and women who give it life and meaning."

PREFACE

THE SAN DIEGO SUBURB of La Jolla lies some thirteen miles north of its parent city, at a point where the coastline dips abruptly inward and arcs gently to the north along a level stretch of beach. The beauty of its physical setting and the region's mild climate have made the community a favorite of vacationers and those retiring from more rigorous climes and responsibilities, so that La Jolla has long been regarded as one of the "resort towns" of the California coast. There is speculation now that this sleepy, leisurely atmosphere is bound to change, for in 1964, one of the newest branches of the University of California was established here. If U.C.S.D. (for San Diego) grows as scheduled, it will have some twenty-seven thousand students by the year 1995. Already students, faculty, and supporting personnel have begun to arrive. In the fall of 1966 some 1470 undergraduate students were enrolled in the first of the university's twelve colleges, Revelle, and the number was expected to almost double with the opening of the second college, John Muir, in 1967. It is for these newcomers, especially, that the authors have collected and written down this somewhat informal history of the Scripps Institution of Oceanography.

Scripps Institution has been a La Jolla landmark practically since the turn of the century, and in scientific circles, at least, has brought as much renown as have the town's celebrated Cove and picturesque Riviera-like cliffs. The institution formed the nucleus of faculty, administration and facilities around which the new university began to develop; without Scripps and the ability and foresight of its leadership it is doubtful that U.C.S.D. would have come to La Jolla at all.

In these days when full-grown institutions spring up within a few years, when a legislative appropriation can create a giant university almost overnight, the struggles of a small research institution to establish a foothold and gather together enough people and equipment to explore the vast Pacific Ocean may seem insignificant, even amusing. But it is struggles such as these which have paved the way for the achievements of today, the men formed by the demands of a less-favored era in science who provide much of the leadership for today's great advances. The Scripps Institution of Oceanography and a handful of other research facilities had the answers, or knew where to find them, when great scientific questions were posed by the Second World War and subsequent events. Many scientists feel that a large part of the government's current willingness to sponsor fundamental research and the generosity of its subsidies can be traced to the lessons learned in wartime from men like those who were working at the Scripps Institution. We have attempted, then, to put down what we consider to be an important story before the few written records that remain are displaced and memories are further obscured by the changes occurring so rapidly today. It is a story of which we feel the newcomers—the students and faculty of U.C.S.D., as well as the hundreds of scientists who will make use of the Scripps Institution of Oceanography's fine research facilities—can be justly proud.

We had originally intended to deal only with the institution's early years, with its development until 1925 or so; the reader will note that this early period is given a relatively detailed coverage. One of the authors began to delve into these beginnings in 1961 in order to prepare some radio talks on the institution's history, and was alarmed to find that already the cartons of random letters and reports, of unlabelled photographs and building specifications, were giving way before the deluge of new acquisitions in the battle for library shelf space. "Old-timers" joined with her to label pictures and sort through memories, and a fascinating story of early scientific enterprise began to emerge from the random collection of memorabilia. It seemed to us this was a story which warranted preservation, and so we set out to sift through the assortment of yellowing documents and impress some order on them. Part-way through we were asked to extend our modest efforts and bring the story of Scripps up to the present, so that it might be put forward as U.C.S.D.'s "centennial monograph" in connection with the University of California's hundredth anniversary in 1967-68. So we plunged on into S.I.O.'s accomplishments under directors Vaughan and Sverdrup, into the complexities of science in the Second World War, into the aftermath of reorganization and the great surge in government interest and support. And then it simply became too big for us.

So few were involved in the original Scripps Institution undertaking that we felt we might attempt to sketch the role of each. In later years this became an impossibility. With the advent of the war and the great expansion of oceanographic research which followed it, the history would have to expand to a many-volume work to give each his due. And it would have to be written by someone else. Neither of the authors is a scientist nor purports even to fully comprehend the great changes that have taken place in the last twenty years in oceanography, or the role the Scripps Institution has played in them (although one of the authors has been related to the Scripps faculty by marriage throughout this period). It is with deference that we write even of earlier, more "simple" expeditions and discoveries.

Ideally, scientists should write of scientific history and properly place it in perspective for the reader. But it is the rare scientist who will take time to write more than journal articles or research papers. The lure of the laboratory and the undiscovered is always stronger than the lure of past history and dusty archives, so that it falls to wives and observers like us to dust off the scrapbooks and attempt to write some of it down. We hope the reader will look kindly on our efforts and realize that we have attempted to write a book about science for non-scientists, a book about the problems of university administration for those who would rather ignore them, a book about personalities for those who would rather have hard facts. It is, of course, an impossible task, and we can only hope there will be something of interest in this conglomerate story for almost everybody.

BEATRICE MOULTON
HELEN RAITT

La Jolla, December, 1966

ACKNOWLEDGMENTS

THE AUTHORS could never have written this book without the assistance of countless people, who sorted through their memories and their scrapbooks to help us. We are also grateful to those who read the manuscript along the way, helping to locate errors in fact and expression. The most we can do is to attempt to list the names of those who have contributed many hours of work and provided much encouragement, with our heartfelt thanks.

We are indebted to the following who allowed us time for interviews during the last five years: Robert Arthur, Edna Watson Bailey, Joshua Bailey and the late Mrs. Joshua Bailey, the late Miss Molly Baker, Laura Crandall, Carl Eckart, Mrs. Guy Fleming, Richard Fleming, Denis and Miriam Fox, Edward Hindle, Carl and Laura Hubbs, Chauncey I. Jerabek, Martin Johnson, Myrtle Johnson, Eugene and Katherine La Fond, the late Obie Maler, Mr. and Mrs. George McEwen, Walter Munk, Ruth Ragan, Russell Raitt, Roger and Ellen Revelle, Marston and Peter Sargent, Francis Shepard, the late William T. Skilling, Mrs. Francis Sumner and Claude ZoBell.

We also wish to thank Anne Nutt Baker, Milton Bramlette, Isabel Crosby, Priscilla Duffield, Carolyn Vaughan Fortune, Jeffery Frautschy, Chancellor and Mrs. John Galbraith, James Gilmore, Cy Greaves, Marian Gunning, Mrs. W. W. Hawkins, Florence Henderson, Alice Heyneman, Sam Hinton, Sandra Huszar, Laurence Klauber, Elizabeth Kunkel, Anita Laton, Lon Manar, Effie Michener, Director and Mrs. William Nierenberg, Joseph Reid, Sam Scripps, Mr. and Mrs. Ronald Silveira de Braganza, Mrs. Harry Smithton, Fred Spiess and Gudrun Sverdrup.

Our appreciation goes to those who assisted us with the illustrations: David Crouch, Robert Fisher, Nelson Fuller, Carl Johnson, Eugene La Fond, Neil Marshall, Diana Midlam, James Rupert and Howard Shirley.

We owe a debt to all the librarians who humored our eccentricities, especially to Melvin Voigt, George Vdovin, Joseph Gantner and to the La Jolla Historical Society, Serra Museum and San Diego Public Library.

CONTENTS

ILLUSTRATIONS
(*following page 44*)

Staff and students, 1904
Marine Biological Station at La Jolla Cove, 1905
Director William E. Ritter
Dr. Fred Baker
Edward Wyllis Scripps
Miss Ellen Browning Scripps
The first ship built, *Alexander Agassiz*
George H. Scripps building from a distance
George H. Scripps building, close up
Director's first home in the Scripps building
Scripps Institution for Biological Research after 1916
Director T. Wayland Vaughan
Staff in 1936
Director Harald U. Sverdrup
The sailing ship, *E. W. Scripps*
Gulf of California cruise, 1939
Scripps Institution of Oceanography, 1938
Director Carl Eckart
Three new ships, 1948
The ship *Horizon*, 1950
Work on operation "Mid-Pac"
Scripps Institution of Oceanography, 1952
Director Roger Revelle and Professor Hans Pettersson
Scripps Institution of Oceanography, 1959
Director Fred N. Spiess
Floating instrument platform, *FLIP*
Director William A. Nierenberg
Scripps Institution and Revelle College, 1966
Scripps Marine Facility and the newest ship, *Alpha Helix*
Expedition Chart Track, 1950-1965
Ritter Hall and Sverdrup Hall, 1966

[xv]

INTRODUCTION

HELEN RAITT AND BEATRICE MOULTON have written splendidly of the magnificent history of a great institution. Its present status in the world as a leading center of oceanography is a tribute to the citizens of San Diego who helped in its creation and supported it all through the years.

It is a paradox that the country's oldest institution of oceanography should have been born in San Diego at a time when the community was isolated from the great centers of learning in the world—and created by instinct and a certain appreciation of the importance of the science. Although the first degree earned in the Institution was not until 1930 it is also a tribute to the Regents of the University of California that at each crucial juncture in the history of the Institution they made the right decision that enabled the Institution to grow, prosper and maintain its lead. We must also recognize Scripps' good fortune and good luck in having a series of directors who accomplished great things with very limited resources. Among these accomplishments was the development of a real school of oceanography in the United States resulting in the handful of graduates of the Institution who at the present time hold important positions and perform vital functions throughout the United States and upon whom our government will have to depend in first measure for the expansion that is everywhere predicted in the ocean sciences.

However, the director is not a historian, his job is not to look at the past but to guess the future and it is a promising future. This future, of course, will be built on our students and they are coming to us better trained, better motivated and more mature than ever before. It is unfortunate that we are only able to accept about ten percent of the students that apply. We probably will never really be able to regain our ability to deal with the demand because of the belated recognition of this accelerated interest.

These fortunate students will have instruments and will be involved in research programs that seemed only idle hopes just ten years ago. The new oceanographic vessels that are just now beginning to appear are completely designed from the keel up for the purpose and are not the hand-me-downs that served so marginally, if valiantly, in the past. Their positions will be determined at all times to a fraction of a nautical mile by a new kind of celestial navigation—that computed from an orbiting satellite whose result will be fed into the shipboard computer along with a mass of other data taken simultaneously.

The students and their professors will be deeply involved in a whole variety of new and major programs. The Deep Sea Drilling Project is just getting under way. First stages will involve taking cores of several thousand feet in length across the width of both oceans. This will provide years of important research for almost all of the disciplines in oceanography. There will be a great expansion of research in the air-sea interaction. Aside from its intrinsic importance to the science of oceanography and meteorology it will move us in the direction of deeper insight into the possibilities of long-range weather prediction and perhaps weather control. Buoy networks covering large areas of the ocean will be used, and eventually some perfected form of ocean satellite will be brought to bear on the problem in some significant way.

The oceanographer is a hardy breed of scientist. He takes his measurements and does his science with instruments and methods which fundamentally differ little from those of his counterpart on land, but under physical circumstances which are far more difficult. His platform and his stomach are both unstable and despite many years of growing expertize he has developed very few really new techniques for getting either himself or his instruments in or out of the sea with any facility. There is much lost time and motion in the process. One of the great steps forward will be large, fixed installations—perhaps something close to where the Scripps Canyon meets the La Jolla Canyon—which will serve as a major *in situ* laboratory for a whole variety of oceanographic purposes, medicine, physiology, marine biology, ecology, physical oceanography, in-shore processes, ocean engineering and so on. If this comes to pass, the great value to Scripps of being part of the new campus of the University of California, San Diego will be most evident, for the maximum return from these efforts will only be realized in the full interaction of the Institution with the Medical School, the Department of Engineering and the other departments of the campus. This relationship has already borne fruit in many ways and as I write these lines the ALPHA HELIX is well on its way on its second expedition, this time to the upper Amazon with a program heavily dependent on a variety of biological and medical disciplines.

The Institution has served its country and its state in many, many ways. From what one can see of the future the Institution and its graduates will be called on more and more to deal with the broad general problems that our society will have to face. Some of these are involved with our environment, food and water for an exploding world population, and the fuller exploitation of the mineral wealth of the earth. These problems are very closely linked to the science of oceanography but I feel that the oceanographer's contributions will go beyond this. By virtue of his training he must sense these problems in a global way. Where his role in the past has been that of the specialist in his own field, his role in the future will more and more be that of the generalist whose experience and viewpoint will be sought from all sides and in all echelons of government, both national and international because of his interdisciplinary viewpoint.

With all of this we can only visualize a future of increased aims and goals and better equipment for these—both intellectual and material. It is gratifying to see the field mature to the point where it includes the best of the basic disciplines and it is equally gratifying to know that there remain vast areas yet to be explored with their own special discoveries that give the field of oceanography unique characteristics and the work at Scripps its own satisfaction.

WILLIAM A. NIERENBERG

SCRIPPS INSTITUTION OF OCEANOGRAPHY

CHAPTER I

CAMPING AND COLLECTING

———

IN 1885 A YOUNG TEACHER, William Emerson Ritter, left his native Wisconsin and journeyed to California, largely because of a textbook on geology. He was in pursuit not of minerals, however, but of ideas, for Joseph Le Conte, the textbook's author, was then Professor of Natural Sciences at the small and struggling University of California, where the young man hoped to continue his studies. Later events proved that no distance was too great for Ritter to travel once his active mind had fastened on an idea, or set of ideas, in which he found meaning. It is fortunate for the world of science, and in particular for the realm of oceanic investigation, that the ideas which attracted him most strongly were those of biology, which was for him, in its broadest sense, the "science of life."

The story of the Scripps Institution of Oceanography, in its early years, is so closely the story of W. E. Ritter's pursuit of an idea that it is impossible to separate the two. This is not to say that he alone was responsible for establishing what is now the world's largest oceanographic institution; without the considerable support and guidance of others he could never have gone so far. But even those most closely associated with him in the venture took small credit for themselves. Some years later Dr. Fred Baker, who had been one of the three or four people most vitally involved in the institution's founding, said of Ritter and his role:

I believe . . . that few institutions of this character have grown up which more fully express the ideas and ideals of one man than does this one. Rarely assertive, always happily good-natured, ready at all times to listen to others and to defer to their judgment, nevertheless, he was the dominating force which drove us all to the goal which he had set.[1]

What was the goal which inspired Ritter and around which he rallied support? In words it seems so clear and simple as to be almost attainable—a biological survey of that part of the Pacific Ocean adjacent to the coast of California, prosecuted as systematically, as continuously, as protractedly and as broadly as facilities would permit. Later, investigations of the physical properties of the ocean became part of the survey and broadened the base of the already infinite undertaking. It was an overwhelming task even to begin, but Ritter did begin, as early as 1892, when he and a small group of students set up a tent laboratory for the summer at Pacific Grove. By this time he had been appointed head of the University of California's newly-formed Department of Zoology.

When he arrived in California in 1885, Ritter spent the first year teaching in Fresno in order to earn his tuition, then entered the university at Berkeley in 1886, where he continued to tutor high school students part-time to support himself. The thirty-year-old Ritter was a serious student, and obtained his B.S. degree within two years. His graduating class in 1888 consisted of eighty-one men and three women students; the entire student body of the twenty-year-old institution numbered only about seven hundred. For a year Ritter stayed on to do graduate work, then in 1889 was awarded a scholarship at Harvard University, where he spent the next two years. When he returned to Berkeley in 1891 it was to accept the chairmanship of the new Zoology department and to marry Mary Bennett, a young medical doctor he had met that first year at Fresno. Unknowingly taking a step which was to influence the future course of their lives, the couple took a honeymoon trip to San Diego.

As the subject of his PhD thesis at Harvard, Ritter had chosen the retrograde eyes of the Blind Goby, a rare fish species which could be found under the rocks below Point Loma at the entrance to San Diego Bay.[2] Combining work with pleasure Ritter and his bride spent at least one day collecting specimens, and the young scientist was thus introduced to the wealth of material for biological study which the area offered. Another significant feature of this honeymoon trip was that Ritter became acquainted, through his wife, with Doctors Fred and Charlotte Baker, who lived in Roseville on Point Loma. Thus began an association which, more than ten years later, would take on such importance in the establishment of a base for Ritter's studies of marine life.

Meantime, during the decade following his appointment to the university, Ritter and other members of the Department of Zoology explored the Pacific coastline in search of a likely spot for a seaside laboratory. "Imperfectly as had any of the fields of zoology in Western America been cultivated," wrote Ritter, looking back some twenty years later, "the least studied of all had been the teeming life of the great ocean on whose margin the University is located. This consideration was of itself a strong incentive to marine investigations."[3]

At the outset there was little to distinguish the University of California's seaside laboratory from those maintained by other institutions, except, perhaps, that it was more migratory and less well-equipped than others. But the nature of the biological studies, and the methods employed in carrying them out, followed the pattern established at such laboratories as that at Woods Hole, Massachusetts, and the Stazione Zoologica on the Bay of Naples.[4] In these and similar institutions scattered throughout the world in those days individual scientists spent a portion of their time, most frequently the summer, pursuing their own biological studies on specimens of marine life. These laboratories had no particular program *as institutions*; they merely provided a convenient location, working space and equipment for those scientists who wished to make use of their facilities.

As none of the established biological stations was within reach of Ritter and his students, and as the great Pacific Ocean lying virtually untouched at their doorstep offered a unique challenge, in 1892 the Department of Zoology appropriated $200 for summer investigations of ocean life. With this sum a commodious canvas tent, planned as a portable laboratory which could be set up wherever the biologists might settle during the next few years, was purchased and first erected at Pacific Grove on the Monterey Peninsula. San Francisco Bay, despite its proximity to Berkeley, had been rejected as a site because, being virtually landlocked, it did not offer truly oceanic conditions, and the two large rivers emptying their sediments into it contributed to the absence of sea life. Also in 1892, the Timothy Hopkins laboratory of Stanford University was established at Pacific Grove. The Stanford facilities, which remained permanently at Pacific Grove, were larger and in general much more impressive than the flimsy University of California structure of canvas and wood. But it was the work that mattered, and throughout the summer both groups of investigators diligently collected, sorted and examined the local fauna.

The next year the Berkeley graduate and undergraduate students, again under Ritter's direction, folded their tent and moved south to set up camp at Avalon Bay on Santa Catalina Island, west of Los Angeles. The beautiful setting and balmy climate afforded much after-hours diversion for the group, who stored their tent-laboratory in a church basement in hopes of returning the next year to pursue their profitable and enjoyable studies. The summer of 1894, however, found the Ritters in Europe at the start of their sabbatical leave, and no official university investigations were carried on that year. Unofficially, however, three of the students who had been at Avalon the previous summer explored the coast to the north as far as Eureka. In 1895, while the Ritters were still in Europe, a party of six set up a laboratory at San Pedro, the harbor for the Los Angeles area and a place which had attracted the biologists on their trip to Catalina. This summer's work strengthened the belief that Southern California afforded especially favorable conditions for marine investigations.

Between 1896 and 1901, although there were no organized parties nor a seaside laboratory, various members of the zoology department made numerous collecting excursions and brought back reports on possible locations for a permanent laboratory as well as specimens of marine life. In 1899 Ritter, as a member of the Harriman Expedition to Alaska, was able to explore Puget Sound and much of the coastline further north.

Railroad magnate E. H. Harriman, ordered by his doctors to take a complete rest, had chartered a steamer, refitted it for the needs of his family and guests, including his doctor and pastor, and planned a trip to Alaska, beyond the reach of telegraph wires. To make the trip count for more than pleasure, Harriman invited forty scientists, artists and writers to go along as his guests. It had been decided to include a representative of every profession and branch of science which might benefit from the trip, and Ritter had been selected as an expert on marine invertebrates.

A large amount of valuable material was collected on the expedition, and the results were published in the next few years at Harriman's expense. During the day the boat was virtually turned over to the scientists; Ritter described the hurricane deck as "strewn fore and aft, on sunny days, with skeletons, bird and mammal skins, shells and rocks, sea weeds and plant driers." The combined pleasure cruise-scientific expedition was a unique experience for everyone involved. "Those who have some familiarity with the rather stereotyped duties of a ship's crew," wrote Ritter in an article for the *University Chronicle*, "will appreciate the consternation that might be produced among officers and men by having three dozen crazy naturalists turned loose among them, and at the same time receiving orders that they must hold themselves strictly at the mercy of their tormentors."[5] As the ship made at least forty stops during the two months voyage for the purposes of collecting, Ritter was enabled to make a rather comprehensive survey of the waters along the coast. When the trip was over Ritter had greatly increased the university's collection of marine invertebrates and his own store of knowledge of the Pacific coastline; in addition he had formed lasting associations with many of the leading scientists of his day.

By 1900 members of the University of California's zoology department had thus explored the shores of the Pacific, with varying degrees of thoroughness, from the Mexican border to Alaska. Gradually they had come to the conclusion that the bay at San Pedro was the most favorable location of any in which they had carried on investigations for further marine biological activity. Late in that first year of the century Ritter launched a determined effort to create a permanent, well-supported seaside station, presumably to be located at San Pedro. On December 12, he outlined his proposal in a letter to Benjamin Ide Wheeler, president of the university, who approved the plan and agreed to communicate with certain Los Angeles alumni. Initially he would not commit the university to any financial support. "Our friends in Southern California ought to raise $2500 for you at least," he wrote.[6]

Fortunately a few Los Angeles friends of the university did become interested, and about $1800 was raised for the summer's work. When it became obvious in the spring that the private subscriptions would not meet the expenses of the projected summer session, the university added to the fund. Unlike previous summers, formal classes in zoology were offered in both 1901 and 1902, not only because the investigations offered a natural opportunity for instruction, but because it was hoped that the fees ($10 tuition, $5 laboratory fee) would help cover the costs of the instructors' travel to and from

Berkeley. Remembering this tight financial situation ten years later, Ritter recalled, "Only the smallest and crudest beginnings could be made. But even a beginning would be something, and confidence in the soundness and workableness of an idea gives a sort of magnitude and robustness to what is initially small and weak. After having gathered together such sums as we could we went at the undertaking buoyantly . . ."[7]

The summer of 1901 was indeed the beginning of something, for although Ritter, his associates and students had set up a seaside laboratory before, there had not been much organization in their efforts. They now felt, with confidence in their choice of location and familiarity with the methods and equipment to be used, that they were ready to begin a continuing study of the life of the Pacific Ocean and the physical conditions surrounding that life. "In view of the importance of the field, and the meagreness of previous investigations in it," Ritter wrote to President Wheeler, "it seemed best to plan the summer's work as though it were the beginning of a detailed biological survey of the coast of California, even though no assurance could be had of being able to continue the work beyond this season."[8]

In view of the vastness of the undertaking some boundaries had to be set. It was decided in 1901 to limit operations on the biological side to dredging and trawling in depths not to exceed one hundred fathoms, while on the hydrographic side no more than temperature and density determinations were attempted. This work required a boat, and an open gasoline launch, the *Elsie*, was rented and kept busy during the two months of the session. For laboratory work on land, and for classes, a "little old bath-house" and a neighboring building on the sand pit separating San Pedro Bay from the open sea were rented and reconstructed.

Ritter was particularly fortunate, as he began the intensive survey which had been taking shape in his mind, in having as associates in the Department of Zoology men who were thoroughly sympathetic with his views. Two of these, Frank Bancroft and Harry B. Torrey, were his own former students, who on reaching "scientific maturity," had joined the staff of their *alma mater*. The other member of the dedicated foursome was Charles A. Kofoid, who had come to California in 1900 from the University of Illinois. The young biological venture may have been poor in financial assets, but it possessed a wealth of scientific talent.

Kofoid, experienced in marine and aquatic biology, took charge of the work at sea. Eighty-five stations were occupied by the forty-foot launch, chiefly off San Pedro and around Catalina Island. Ritter, remembering his own observations of ten years before and desiring to follow up other favorable reports of San Diego Bay, wanted to explore that region before making a final decision about the site of a permanent laboratory. In addition to making observations and collections at some forty stations with the *Elsie,* the ship's company spent a day or two ashore at San Diego.[9] There Kofoid found Dr. Fred Baker, one of Ritter's few acquaintances in the town, who expressed great interest in the biological station and its program. Baker even had Kofoid address a meeting of the Tuesday Club, made up of some of San Diego's leading business and professional men, on marine exploration. In a talk which Baker later described, Kofoid told of a contemplated biological station which would "equal and surpass the greatest one in the world located at Naples. There are to be very extensive Aquaria and this element will make it a show place for the visiting public ... and the plan further contemplates maintaining a vessel large enough to sound, fish and dredge in any portion of the Pacific Ocean."[10] Throughout the visit Dr. Baker insisted that San Diego was probably the best place on the whole coast of California for such a station. Kofoid returned to San Pedro enthusiastic about the biological merits of the more southerly location.

Meanwhile San Pedro, almost a hundred miles to the north, proved most satisfactory as far as the work was concerned. That summer, for the first time within the memories of the people living in the area,[11] a Peridinium "epidemic" occurred, causing a "red tide" during the day and brilliant phosphorescence at night, which lasted almost two months. The scientists undertook a study of the phenomenon, noting the duration, geographical extent and effects on other forms of life of this mass visitation of minute organisms. The professors and advanced students also continued investigations on various specific groups of marine animals, furnished with ample material from the rich hauls brought in by the *Elsie.* A few scientists not connected with the university, including Russian diatomist W. C. Adler-Mereschkowsky, used the laboratory facilities for various periods of time during the summer in pursuing independent studies.

One incidental discovery, which Ritter described as "of so much significance as to make it among the most important results of the season's operations,"[12] was that the island of Santa Catalina had undergone subsidence. About three-quarters of a mile off Long Point, on the north side of the island, the dredge had brought up many smooth, rounded cobble stones, indicating the presence under forty-five fathoms of water of an ancient shoreline. Though the finding was geological rather than biological, Ritter published the evidence and conclusions reached in an article in *Science* in 1901.

The summer had been quite successful from the scientific standpoint, but despite all efforts at fund-raising the department ended the session with a sizable deficit, which Berkeley patron Mrs. Phoebe Hearst helped make up the following spring. Prospects of finances for the next year were even less promising, but Ritter hopefully made plans to bring the department back to San Pedro in 1902 to do as much work as possible. He contacted E. H. Harriman in search of funds, but found that although the millionaire railroad man might have been persuaded to join with other supporters to a limited extent, he was unwilling to take on the burden of the financial responsibility for the project.

A month or two before the 1902 summer work was to begin, Ritter received an invitation from Fred Baker to bring the summer session to San Diego and set up a laboratory in the Roseville schoolhouse. The difficulty of transferring equipment and making necessary improvements in the building at so late a date, as well as the fear that the move might deter some of the students from the Los Angeles area, caused Ritter and his associates to decide against Baker's offer in 1902. "This is not to be understood to mean that we do not contemplate further work at that place," Ritter wrote to Baker. "Your kind and very lively interest in the matter may, I hope, bear fruit yet."[13]

As there was not sufficient money to rent a launch, biological investigations at San Pedro in 1902 were restricted to littoral, or shoreline, forms of life. Classes were again conducted and everyone kept busy, but it was becoming obvious that, if the survey was to make any progress, it would be necessary to work at collecting funds as well as fauna. The "Los Angeles gentlemen" most interested in the work—J. A. Graves, H. W. O'Melveny, Jacob Baruch, and J. H. Shankland—with Ritter devised a plan of raising $20,000 with which to erect and equip a permanent laboratory. Each member of a committee of businessmen was to work among his own business associates and acquaintances, obtaining the required amount in sums of $500. The subscriptions were made contingent on nearly the whole $20,000 being raised. Despite the best efforts of Ritter and his handful of loyal supporters during the summer of 1902, the attempt had to be given up, for subscriptions could be obtained for only about one-third of the required amount.

Another discouraging development during 1902 was the beginning by the U.S. government of harbor improvements at San Pedro, which would soon destroy the bay's best collecting grounds. The scientists began to realize that the growth of population and commercial activity around the little bay in the next few years would make it practically useless as a site for biological investigations.

Looking for alternatives Ritter attempted to get help from George M. Bowers, the United States Commissioner of Fish and Fisheries in Washington. He had heard that the commission was planning a fisheries station for Southern California, but learned that Congress had not yet allocated any funds for the project. All in all, prospects for the "continuous and long-continued" survey, begun so optimistically the year before, were growing darker at each turn.

Those fates who make it their business to frustrate man's hopes and ambitions, however, had not reckoned on Ritter's strength of purpose. Firmly convinced of the worth of his plan and determined to carry it out, he was confident somehow that the necessary means would be found. In the interim, in woefully inadequate facilities, he and his students and associates did whatever biological research they could. "For the rest," Ritter wrote in 1902, "like Elijah of old, we 'stand before the lord, hungry but full of trust, and therefore expecting the ravens laden with bread and meat to appear at any moment."14

CHAPTER II

THE TEMPTATIONS OF TENT CITY

WITH THE NEW YEAR a solitary raven appeared on the horizon—a renewed invitation from Dr. Fred Baker. Would Ritter consider bringing his biological investigations to San Diego during the summer of 1903? Baker gave assurances that he and others interested in the project could raise the necessary funds if Ritter would indicate his willingness to move from San Pedro. This was an easy concession, for although Ritter had been relatively satisfied with the results of two summers of work at San Pedro, the financial prospects there for 1903 were unpromising. So Ritter returned a prompt and definite answer to Baker in early February: if Baker and his friends would locate and equip a suitable laboratory, and in addition provide $500 for operating expenses, the University of California's Department of Zoology would carry on its summer's activities at San Diego.

This was all Baker needed. Dr. Ritter had suggested that he look into the possibility of using as a laboratory the boathouse of the Coronado Hotel, which had been offered for this purpose to President Wheeler of the university by E. S. Babcock, manager of the Coronado Beach Company. Two days after receiving the suggestion Baker had visited Coronado, conferred with Mr. Babcock about converting the boathouse and possibly using one of the hotel's launches and was sending a comparative appraisal of this and another possible site to Dr. Ritter, complete with diagrams and an estimate of the costs of the changes that would be necessary. Confident that they could raise the minimum amount Ritter had asked for, Baker went on to say that if Ritter would specify what he could do with an additional $300 to $500, it would be helpful to the San Diego fund raisers. The transient marine biological laboratory had found its most enthusiastic and tireless supporter, and Fred Baker had started out on what he was later to consider the most important thing he had ever done.

Not without influence in the youthful San Diego community of some 17,000 people, Baker proceeded to interest others in his scheme. He and his wife Charlotte, also a medical doctor, had come to San Diego in 1888, after taking their medical degrees at the University of Michigan, and practicing briefly in Ohio and New Mexico.[1] In San Diego Dr. Charlotte and Dr. Fred, as they came to be known, were both very active in civic affairs. When Fred Baker first took on Dr. Ritter and his problems he was president of both the San Diego Board of Education and the county medical society, and was involved in numerous other medical, civic and scientific activities. Business and professional men respected Dr. Fred and took seriously his ideas concerning the potential importance of the biological research institution contemplated by the university. The Tuesday Club, which Charles Kofoid had addressed on his visit to San Diego in 1901, yielded many of those most anxious to secure the biological station on a permanent basis for San Diego, and most willing to work for it. That Baker succeeded in convincing community leaders of the value of the laboratory to the city is evidenced by the fact that the Chamber of Commerce set up a special Marine Laboratory Committee for the purposes of fund raising.

But it was not wholly from the standpoint of civic duty that Fred Baker became such a confirmed advocate of bringing Ritter and his biological station to San Diego. An enthusiastic amateur naturalist, Baker specialized in conchology. He had collected shells everywhere he had been, and in his younger years had visited a number of out-of-the-way places. At the time the biological station first came to San Diego he already had one of the finest collections of shells in the area, and his competence and knowledge in this field were widely recognized. In 1911 he was to serve as surgeon and conchologist on the Stanford Expedition to Brazil, headed by J. C. Branner.

Fond of collecting and studying sea life himself, then, Dr. Baker knew what personal satisfaction he could derive from the opportunity to observe and work with researchers of the professional standing of Ritter and his associates. In promoting their work, which he sincerely believed was important, he would also have a chance to participate in activities he enjoyed. He had explored the beaches and rocky shores of San Diego Bay, and knew it to be a rich collecting ground. It is evident from his early letters, full of thoughtful plans and meticulous reports of his efforts at putting the station on a firm basis, that he was sincerely convinced that San Diego was the most likely site on the Southern California coast for a permanent laboratory. He hoped that by inducing Ritter and the others to come for a summer he could demonstrate to them the advantages of selecting the San Diego area as the final location for their biological station.

With this hope in mind, then, he continued in that spring of 1903 to convey his enthusiasm to others. His most willing and able helpmate in this endeavor was H. P. Wood, Secretary of the San Diego Chamber of Commerce, who had made the first visit to Mr. Babcock at Coronado with him. Wood accompanied him on almost all of his visits to wealthier citizens in quest of funds. Seemingly their task was not too difficult. "Only one man approached has refused," Baker reported in one letter. "It took two of us just seventy-five seconds to get a hundred dollars yesterday morning."[2] With restrained excitement he began one letter with an account of a visit he and Wood had made to a "wealthy rancher" who had promised $500. Later he identified the rancher as newspaper publisher Edward W. Scripps, and expressed the hope that Ritter could meet him when he came to San Diego to look over the proposed laboratory and give a talk designed to interest potential supporters. "He takes no interest in biology," Baker added, "but has come to the rescue generously. If you could interest him and his sister, Miss Ellen Scripps, they might put your whole project on its feet ... They are reputed to be worth several millions."[3]

In late March Ritter made his visit, met at the San Diego train station by an excited Baker who put him aboard his son Rob's launch and ferried him to the Baker home on Point Loma. Ritter spent a busy few days—looking over the Coronado Hotel's boathouse at Glorieta Bight, giving a public lecture complete with lantern slides about his work, exploring the bay by boat and fishing for specimens. He also met with the members of the chamber of commerce fund raising committee.

When he returned to his duties at Berkeley Ritter was considerably more excited about plans for the summer. In San Diego he was meeting the kind of interest and support he had always wished to have. Drawing up a list of modifications necessary to make the fifty-foot-square boathouse at Glorieta Bight into a biological laboratory, he sent them off to San Diego. Manager Babcock balked at a few of the more expensive changes, such as making a piece of the porch into an additional room, and in his letter explaining this Baker suggested ways in which the chamber of commerce committee might make the improvements with their own funds.

Soon the use of a launch capable of deep sea dredging became an issue of importance. Without the use of a boat the laboratory's work during the summer would be limited to whatever material they could obtain from shore and pile collection, and the results would indicate only in a general way the suitability of San Diego Bay for a permanent location. Babcock had at one time offered the use of one of the hotel launches, but as this became less certain and Baker's efforts to interest others in providing the free use of a launch were unsuccessful, Baker obtained the services of Manuel Cabral, whom he considered the best and most intelligent of the Portuguese fisherman in San Diego. Cabral would use a rented schooner, the *Lura*, to make collections for the laboratory during the six weeks summer session.

By late May nearly everything was ready—the promised subscriptions for the most part collected, equipment shipped from the San Pedro laboratory and stored in the renovated boathouse, and accounts settled up to date. Many San Diego merchants had donated building materials and laboratory supplies or had sold them to the committee at a substantial discount. The summer session began in mid-June, and with the work actually underway at last, Baker and the other San Diego sponsors were able to breathe a little more easily.

Baker had wondered if there would be too many distractions for the scientists in the resort town of Coronado. They lived and worked in the midst of Tent City, a popular vacation retreat for those who couldn't afford to stay at the sumptuous Hotel del Coronado. The strand along little Glorieta Bight, in front of the hotel and on either side of the boathouse, was crowded with tents which could be rented completely furnished for fifty cents a day. At night there were concerts, dances, performances by magicians and ventriloquists—a host of tempting diversions for the most dedicated students of science.

Despite such distractions, however, as far as Ritter and his San Diego supporters were concerned, the summer's work was most satisfactory. In addition to Ritter, who continued his work on the Tunicata and Enteropneustra, the scientific staff included C. A. Kofoid, working chiefly on the Protozoa; H. B. Torrey on the Coelenterata; C. O. Esterly on the Copepoda; J. F. Bovard as Kofoid's assistant; J. N. Evans who made hydrographic observations and acted as preparator; two student assistants and D. A. Carlson of Stanford and B. M. Davis of the Los Angeles Normal School, who used the laboratory in connection with their independent studies. Due in part to the Coronado location, which was relatively far from the area's best rocky collecting grounds, it had been decided to devote most of the summer's efforts to investigations of free-floating forms of plankton rather than those forms fixed along the shore or at the bottom. Collecting was left to Cabral and his helper, who evidently performed this task most ably.

Ritter could cite only two minor drawbacks in the boathouse laboratory itself—the building, which was built on piles over the water, was not steady enough for microscopic work with high magnifying lenses, and the lack of running sea water made it impossible to carry on certain kinds of work which would have been valuable. But he was able to say in his report to President Wheeler that "all things considered the summer's work has been the most satisfacory of any that the department has yet carried on."

More important as far as his San Diego backers were concerned, Ritter had come to the conclusion that San Diego was an extremely good location for a permanent marine biological laboratory. "I am not going to report now that San Diego is unquestionably the best place on earth for such an institution," he said. "I am simply going to say that is is undoubtedly an excellent place from several points of view—one of the best."[4] The department's investigations had shown the plankton and the bottom fauna to be rich and varied, with tropical as well as northern forms represented. The abyssal depth of the sea could be reached a short distance from shore, and climatic conditions were such that a small vessel could work almost every day for at least ten months of the year. "There can be no doubt," Ritter concluded in his report to the Chamber of Commerce Committee, "that a laboratory capable of great things for biological science might be built at San Diego."

A rich collecting ground as far as marine animals were concerned, the San Diego area also appeared favorable for the collection of funds. A total of $1300, enough to finance two weeks of work during the Christmas vacation in addition to the summer session, had been raised in 1903. There was evidence that this financial support reflected for the most part a continuing interest in the establishment of the station, and that there would be little difficulty in financing another year's work and possibly in endowing a permanent location. Ritter, in thanking the San Diego citizens responsible for this support,[5] was well aware of Baker's vital role in the summer's success. "Indeed," he wrote, "I have all the time felt myself to be merely the superintendent of one of Dr. Baker's numerous enterprises."[6]

In Fred Baker, Ritter had found a hard-working organizer, a professional man willing to spend long hours in attending to the details of setting up the biological laboratory. Dr. Fred could not give much in the way of financial assistance on his own, but fortunately he knew which citizens of San Diego had more ample resources, and he was not afraid to go "begging," to use his own term, to obtain their support for the marine biological laboratory.

Even Baker and his collecting companion H. P. Wood were unaware at the time, however, of the importance of their decision to contact E. W. Scripps that spring of 1903. With his gift of $500 Scripps had made the largest single contribution to the work of the summer, and in his conversations with Baker and Ritter developed a sincere interest in what the "university men" hoped to accomplish with the funds. On August 2, while the work was in progress, Ritter and Wood were invited to lunch at Miramar Ranch to confer with E. W. and his sister Ellen.

This was the first of numerous visits Ritter was to make to the sprawling Spanish-style ranch house on more than two thousand acres of land which Scripps had acquired to the northeast of San Diego, well inland from the damp sea breezes. The publisher had chosen this site in 1892 on a visit to San Diego, which he described as "a busted, broken-down boom town, . . . probably more difficult of access than any other spot in the whole country." From this isolated and extraordinary winter home, E. W., as he was familiarly known, directed his newspaper empire and kept track of his many and varied sideline interests. He would summon his lieutenants, his political cronies, and people who simply interested him to conferences in the panelled library or huge central patio at Miramar. In this house of thirty-six large rooms great business mergers were concluded and political campaigns were planned; and here the dreams of a permanent laboratory for the study of the Pacific Ocean began to take on the shape of reality. During that first afternoon a temporary organizing committee was formed.

As officers and seemingly the sole members of this committee, Ritter, Baker and Wood were to contact and bring together in a meeting those citizens of San Diego they felt might be interested in forming an association to promote the proposed biological investigations and willing to guarantee them financially. Always the businessman, Scripps decided that a small capital investment would be necessary even in these very early stages, and placed $100 at the disposal of the committee. It is recorded that his sister Ellen provided "a like amount." Miss Scripps' backing at this point was largely the product of her brother's endorsement of the project, though she was later to make substantial contributions on her own. For the time being the fact that E. W.—eighteen years younger and her own family favorite—thought the undertaking one worthy of support was enough for Miss Ellen.

If Ellen Scripps was willing to trust her brother's judgment in the matter of the biological station, she knew that there had been and would again be many instances when E. W. turned to her for advice and support. She had practically raised this troublesome younger brother on the family farm in Rushville, Illinois, and when E. W. had left the farm in 1872 to work with his older brothers on the struggling Detroit *Tribune*, Ellen was not long in joining them. Proofreading, writing, and always lending her advice and judgment as her brothers built up the family newspaper empire, Miss Ellen seemed to have a native business ability which eventually enabled her to turn her meagre savings and few shares in the business into a sizable fortune. E. W. never ceased to consult her in the major decisions it fell to him as owner and entrepreneur to make, and indeed considered her a kind of partner. "I know, and I always knew," E. W. wrote years later, "that whatever my sister had I could get from her by the asking. Therefore it made no practical difference to me whether the money earned by myself went into my sister's pocket or my own."[7]

Thus when Fred Baker and H. P. Wood approached him on the subject of bringing the University of California's marine biological laboratory to San Diego, it was E. W.'s natural reaction to suggest that they also contact his sister Ellen in the matter. "We . . . secured a promise of $500 and advice to call on his sister," Baker reported of that first visit, "as she had more money than he, and fewer expenses."[8]

In late August, 1903, when Dr. Ritter had returned to the Berkeley campus after his successful summer's work at Coronado, Ellen and her sister Miss Virginia Scripps paid him a visit at the university. Ritter was surprised and delighted, and took the opportunity to draw Miss Ellen more closely into his plans. "I took them home with me, after showing them about the university," Ritter wrote Baker the next day, "got Miss Ellen into my study alone and succeeded surely in working up her interest still further, and also in giving her more insight into our plans and needs. There is no doubt about the genuineness of her interest and the intelligence of it too . . . I do not believe the idea of making the whole enterprise hers, so that it might be named after her, has seriously entered into her thoughts as yet."[9]

Meanwhile Baker and Wood were working up interest in the San Diego area. They had obtained $250 that first summer from Homer H. Peters, an easterner who had come to San Diego for a rest after amassing a fortune in the grain brokerage business. Although Peters and E. W. Scripps had together provided more than half of the $1300 total the Chamber of Commerce committee had raised, the two businessmen had never become acquainted. In mid-September Baker, Wood, their fellow committeeman J. N. Newkirk and Peters went to Miramar Ranch, and the meeting which took place found E. W. in the role of persuader and promoter on behalf of the biological station. Baker sent Ritter a glowing account of the meeting:

Mr. Peters started in to inquire if he (Scripps) knew different people in Detroit and it transpired that both went to Detroit the same year, 1872, to make their start, that Peters was a crony of one of Scripps' brothers and of McRae of the league, that they had worked with the same men along different lines. They affiliated like two old college mates. All of this before and at lunch. Later Mr. Wood stated our matter. Then Mr. Scripps became the most enthusiastic advocate of the crowd. He said to Mr. Peters, "Now you must put yourself at the head of this thing and make it go. Some of us are willing to help, but we want a man of affairs, one who has made a notorious success in his own business to assure us that no mistakes will be made, and that it will succeed. Dr. Baker and a lot of professional men may take hold of this and it will go very slowly indeed, or it won't go at all, but if businessmen of ample means take hold it will succeed. You and I know that the easiest thing in the world is to raise money, but the right men must go after it. Be the head of it and take the credit for making it a success. This thing if it is worked right will give you an international reputation, for we are going to make this the biggest thing of its kind in the world.

[19]

"Now, I can't take the lead in this thing ... I am into county roads or I might go into this, but I can't, so you have got to do it. We will make you chairman of the Finance Committee, and you have got to make it go. Then when you find out what has to be done you can come out here and hold me up, and we will get the money. It won't take much to begin on. I don't believe they ought to spend over $2000 in the next six months, nor more than $15,000 in the next two years. If I had a hundred thousand dollars in hand I wanted to give them, I would not give them over $2000. I could tell by the way they spent that how they deserved the other $98,000.

"I wouldn't try for a fine building. Any shack will do if there is room enough, but let's have work. Then, when we have learned by a few mistakes, we can spread out and make a big thing. This will throw you in with college people, and they are fine people to meet. And you will get more satisfaction out of it than from anything you can do."[10]

It is hard to imagine anyone withstanding this verbal onslaught from so strong a personality as E. W. Scripps, and Homer Peters was no exception. He protested mildly that he knew nothing of biology, but before he left Miramar Ranch had agreed to take any position given him, do his share and "be one of five to insure the success of the thing." The Marine Biological Association of San Diego was in the making, and plans took shape for a formal organizational meeting.

There was some difficulty in arranging a time and place that would fit in with the schedules of these busy men, but eventually a date was set—September 24, 1903—and Ritter was duly informed and sent a list of the invitees. Those invited constitute a virtual social register of the San Diego of those days. Included were such notables as George W. Marston, Julius Wangenheim, J. D. Spreckels, and U. S. Grant, Jr. Baker urged Ritter to come down the day before the meeting if he had to "close down the university for a few days,"[11] so that they might discuss the form and personnel of the organization they hoped to set up. Enthusiasm was running high; Peters unfortunately had business in the east which would prevent his attending the meeting, but on E. W.'s insistence he had agreed to accept the presidency of the proposed association *in absentia*, and this was taken as a guarantee of substantial financial support on his part. The interest and support of E. W. and Ellen Scripps seemed also to be guaranteed, and if even a handful of other wealthy San Diegans could be persuaded to join with these three, the success of the venture was assured.

Ritter arrived in San Diego the evening preceding the meeting armed with a report outlining the scientific policy which in his judgment should be marked out for the biological station. Also included was an estimate of the initial expense and the modest annual amount necessary to set the project on its feet. It is not hard to imagine the speculation Ritter and Fred Baker engaged in as they went over the agenda for the meeting, now that the finances were available to turn at least some of their dreams into reality.

Attendance at the next day's meeting proved to be disappointingly small, and one of the main orders of business was the setting up of an effort to bring more people out to a meeting scheduled two days later. Ritter did present his report, however, and it met with an encouraging response. The temporary organization was continued until the September 26 meeting, when hopefully a larger number of people could be involved in making the decisions of the permanent association.

The committee on membership must have spent a busy two days, for the meeting which took place at the chamber of commerce rooms two days later was attended by thirty-four people. (Appendix A). This group set up the Marine Biological Association of San Diego and helpfully elected Homer Peters, the businessman, as president of the association, with Ritter to serve as scientific director. Miss Ellen Scripps accepted the vice-presidency; Julius Wangenheim, President of the National Bank of Commerce of San Diego, became treasurer; and Fred Baker was named secretary.

As stated in the minutes, the purpose of the association was to secure "the foundation and endowment of a scientific institution to be known as the San Diego Marine Biological Institution." The general purposes of the institution, in turn, would be "to carry on a biological and hydrographic survey of the waters of the Pacific Ocean adjacent to the coast of Southern California; to build and maintain a public aquarium and museum; and to prosecute such other kindred undertakings as the Board of Trustees may from time to time deem it wise to enter upon." E. W. Scripps and James Mac Mullen of the San Diego *Union*, in addition to the officers already listed, were to serve on the board of trustees.

One of the first actions of the board was to guarantee that work toward the goals of the association would be supported for at least three years. Homer Peters, E. W. and Ellen Scripps each agreed to provide $1500 a year for the three year period, so that the biological station was assured a minimum annual budget of $4500. Although he and other members of the assocation would continue to look for additional sources of income, for the first time Ritter could draw a deep breath and devote the major portion of his thought to planning the survey.

Thus, within the single year of 1903, Dr. Ritter's biological laboratory had been transformed from an itinerant band of summer teacher-researchers into a major scientific undertaking. The seeds had been there all along, but only in San Diego had they found the fertile soil to make them grow and flourish. Only in San Diego had Ritter found others with the vision to recognize and the patience to nurture those seeds of greatness.

CHAPTER III

A DEGREE OF IMPRACTICABILITY

WITH PROBLEMS OF SURVIVAL SOLVED for the time being by the guarantee of funds, the members of the Marine Biological Association were free to turn their attention to matters of long-range significance. One of these was the definition of the biological station's relationship to the University of California, another the selection of a permanent site in San Diego and the construction of a permanent building. E. W. Scripps, although he had said from the beginning that the real responsibility for the station's affairs should rest with "gentlemen and ladies who are interested in biology, and who have leisure time to fill out such as I have not got,"[1] became increasingly involved in making decisions affecting the station's future. In a letter which he drafted to be sent to the board of regents of the state university by the association, E. W. modestly described the extent of that involvement: "It is known that there are a number of public-spirited and wealthy citizens in this locality who will take sufficient interest in this work to provide all the necessary means, providing the University Regents will, by their action in the matter, recognize the value and use of the station by making it a part of, or branch department, of the University."

Neither was there a lack of interest on the part of state and university officials. Since he had become the university's president several years before, Benjamin Ide Wheeler had been an informed, interested and cooperative supporter of Ritter's efforts. He had added the weight of his prestige to requests for funds in the San Pedro days, had made the initial and follow-up contacts with E. S. Babcock in securing the Coronado boathouse, had in short responded as quickly and fully as he could to all requests for assistance. With the university's limited funds he and the board of regents were not in a position to endow a permanent research institution on the scale

Ritter envisioned. The amount of correspondence exchanged, however, makes it clear that both President Wheeler and California Governor George C. Pardee, who as a regent took an active personal part in university affairs, were aware of the station's progress toward permanency, and themselves seriously concerned with the university's role. "If the University could do it, no one would be more pleased than I," wrote Pardee, "But I cannot help remembering that we have not money enough, and can't get it to do all the things for the University that we ought to do."[2] Responsibility other than financial they willingly could and did assume.

In May, 1904, after numerous attempts to arrange such a conference, Governor Pardee met with E. W. Scripps and other Trustees of the San Diego Marine Biological Association at Miramar Ranch. As the guest of the Scrippses, the governor was able to judge firsthand of the sincerity of their interest. Evidently his judgment was favorable, for his earlier reluctance to commit the university to affiliation with so costly a scheme seems to have dissolved. "The comparative advantages of affiliation or union as a co-ordinate department of the State University were discussed," report the minutes, "and it was the sense of the Governor and the Board that affiliation during the formative stage would give more flexibility of management, and that for a short time at least the union with the University should take this form." By the end of the summer a committee of regents, composed of President Wheeler, Governor Pardee, Dr. Chester Rowell of Fresno and Judge Charles W. Slack of San Francisco, with Judge James W. McKinley of Los Angeles as Chairman, had been set up to "cooperate" with the board of the association in managing the business of the institution, until such time as the survey "be made a research department of the University coordinate with other departments of a similar nature."[3] It was agreed that as a token of its interest the university would make loans of scientific equipment and a basic library during the summer sessions, and would provide for the publication of the results of the work.

Also approved at that May meeting were the Articles of Incorporation of the Marine Biological Association of San Diego (Appendix B), which restated the purposes contained in the association's charter, clarified such matters as legal responsibility and location, set limits on the number of directors and made provision for the transfer of the property to the Regents of the University of California, if at a later date this should become advisable. E. W. Scripps had urged the incorporation in order to "enable the Society to do business in a strictly business fashion, instead of conducting its affairs by the parliamentary rules of a tea party,"[4] and was no doubt relieved to see matters so clearly and legally stated.

It was always difficult for Scripps, the man of business, accustomed to contracts and sharply defined relationships and responsibilities, to work with the "professional men" whose world of pure science was to be embodied in the institution. But Drs. Baker and Ritter continued to be the only members of the association whose interest in the undertaking was strong enough to lead them to carry out the detailed work of its day to day operations. Homer Peters, as he regained his health, had also regained a healthy interest in his eastern business enterprises, and was spending less and less time in San Diego. Thus it fell to Baker and Ritter, tediously communicating by means of letters and an occasional telegram, jointly to make the decisions necessary to procure a boat, a building, and a sure future for the marine biological laboratory.

The matter of securing a boat suitable for the work of dredging was vital to the goals of the station, and seemingly the problem was easily solved when, in March of 1904, E. W. offered the use of his yacht, the *Loma*, for the purpose. The *Loma*, which had originally been built as a pilot boat, could easily be adapted to the institution's purposes. E. W. even agreed to provide, in addition to his regular subscription, the $1500 estimated to be necessary to install a gasoline engine in the *Loma* and equip her with scientific apparatus. The only qualification was that the yacht not be so greatly changed as to make it useless as a "pleasure boat," for E. W. wanted to reserve the right to make personal use of the boat should he or his sons have need of it after the 1904 collecting was finished.

The refitting, which had seemed at the outset a simple matter, proved to be more complicated than anyone had anticipated. San Diego was as yet a small town, and though its good harbor had given rise to a small ship-building and ship-outfitting industry, the gasoline engine would have to be made to specification in San Francisco, as would the smaller engine needed for dredging. Finding too tedious the process of writing to Baker for information regarding the placement of the engines, supporting timbers and such, Ritter suggested that they have the *Loma* towed to San Francisco and complete the entire job of refitting there. Baker, undoubtedly glad to be relieved of the task of crawling around in the *Loma's* hold drawing diagrams, readily agreed, obtained Scripps' consent, and "saw the *Loma* outside the kelp" on May 8, 1904. Two weeks later Ritter met her in San Francisco and made arrangements to have her "put on the ways" in a few days time, confident that by midsummer she would be ready for scientific service as a collecting vessel.

The summer session at the Coronado laboratory got underway on May 16, and for a while Ritter talked of delaying his trip to San Diego until the work on the *Loma* was finished, but as June wore on and delays in the shipyard cropped up, he decided to proceed to San Diego ahead of the *Loma* and return to San Francisco whenever the work was completed.

Charles Kofoid had preceded the Ritters to Coronado by more than a month, and under his direction things were running smoothly by the time they arrived. Using his own power salmon boat, the *St. Joseph*, Manuel Cabral was making collections for the laboratory three days a week. The *St. Joseph* was even smaller than the *Lura* which had been used the year before, but as it had been decided to continue the work on plankton, the boat could meet the demands of the 1904 season.

In addition to a few visiting scientists and students, there was a regular staff of twelve, most of whom were continuing the work they had begun the year before. They received sincere encouragement, for one of Dr. Ritter's chief interests at this point was to have some of the results of the work published according to the association's arrangement with the university. This tangible evidence of progress, he felt, would attract the attention of scientists throughout the world to the organized survey they had begun. Hopefully such notice would develop into new forms of assistance, such as part-time use by the station of the U. S. Fisheries steamer *Albatross*. Ritter had spent the month of March, 1904, on board the *Albatross* directing investigations off the San Diego coast, and knew what immense value the use of a ship capable of dredging in great depths would be to the survey. So partly for this reason, by January of 1905 an entire volume of the University of California publications in zoology was issued, devoted solely to work carried on at San Diego, and another compilation was in progress.

Another step was taken in 1904 to put into practice a phase of the projected survey. This was the association's employment of B. M. Davis, who had spent two summers at Coronado, to stay on through the winter of 1904-1905 as resident naturalist. Under his supervision collections were now possible on a year-round basis. Davis set up a small laboratory at Roseville on Point Loma to which Cabral, who also lived in this part of San Diego, could conveniently deliver the material he collected on his weekly trips on the *St. Joseph*.

But what of the *Loma*, at nineteen tons so much better suited for the work of dredging? Why was the admittedly inadequate *St. Joseph* still being used? In the correspondence between Baker and Ritter in October and November of 1904, it becomes apparent that the *Loma* was still on the ways, and that despite six months in San Francisco shipyards she had not yet been transformed from a yacht into a collecting ship. Baker and Ritter were somewhat disturbed, but the explanations offered by the various San Francisco concerns seemed valid, and they patiently waited for the situation to resolve itself. Inevitably, however, E. W. Scripps became aware of the inordinate amount of time the process had taken, and patience was not one of E. W.'s virtues. On December 5 Dr. Fred fearfully forwarded to Ritter the letter he had received that morning from Scripps:

My dear Sir:

"It has been a long time since I have had any report from the boat "LOMA." I cannot believe that any valid excuse can be offered by the contractors who have had the boat in charge.

(Here followed a lengthy estimate of the financial loss caused by the delay) . . . Beyond this, there has been the great annoyance which I have suffered, and which any practical business man would suffer, on account of a treatment so disrespectful as to be equivalent almost to a gratuitous insult.

I do not express this feeling any more from the standpoint of proprietorship in the "LOMA" than from a membership in the Association for which the boat is being fitted out. I am unwilling that the present contractors should have anything more to do with the "LOMA" . . .

I do not wish you to suppose for a moment that I place any blame upon you, or Prof. Ritter. I consider that all of us have equally been treated in an unfair and unbusinesslike way. I suppose that the contractors have rather presumed upon the fact that you were professional men, and have considered it safe to impose upon me for that reason . . .

. . . Your sincerely,
E. W. Scripps

Baker was afraid that the bungling of the *Loma* affair would jeopardize their whole relationship with Scripps, but Ritter had more confidence in the staying-power of E. W.'s commitment. "The portentous condition of our affairs that has developed in the last few days certainly disturbs me a good deal," he wrote Baker, "but I am by no means frightened into entire consternation over it and for this reason: unless I have wholly misjudged E. W. Scripps' character as a whole, he is not the man to be diverted from a main purpose by things of incidental moment. I have so much confidence in his comprehension of, and belief in our scheme as a whole, that I feel pretty sure he will regard this as merely of incidental significance, especially if we are so fortunate as to conduct our end of the affair with wisdom."[5]

In a month or two the storm had subsided; the engines had been tested and approved, and the *Loma* had been safely returned to her berth in the San Diego harbor, ready for use the following summer. But the seas were not yet calm. The cost of the work on the *Loma* exceeded the original $1500 estimate by over $2000, and E. W. grudgingly paid the difference, muttering the while that the association would have to make it good. "I have been so schooled and trained in business that I have acquired the vulgar habits of my vulgar class," wrote E. W. to Ritter of the matter, "and, as a consequence, I am more provoked by any sort of a business mistake, bookkeeping or otherwise, than I could possibly be exhilarated by the feeling that I had helped to discover ten thousand new kinds of bugs."[6]

There also had been a misunderstanding that year over the designing and building of a more adequate laboratory. The Coronado Beach Company had added an extra room to the boathouse for the summer of 1904, and the supporting piles had been braced to make the building more stable, but none of the association's members doubted that after 1904 new facilities must be found or constructed. A makeshift laboratory might suffice for a group of loosely associated individual researchers, but for an ambitious organized survey such as that planned for the station, working conditions must be as nearly ideal as possible. Thus at the May, 1904 meeting of the trustees Ritter had been requested to "have plans drawn for a building large enough to meet the requirements of the association when fully developed but on such a plan that a part can be constructed for immediate use, and added to as the necessity may demand."

Apparently Ritter took more seriously the former clause of this request, while Scripps was especially concerned with the latter, for when Ritter presented the plans drawn by the university architect it was evident that there had been a lack of communication. These plans, submitted in the fall of 1904, called for an imposing two-story edifice costing at least $50,000, and though Scripps could admit that it was "admirably designed, in the interior, for the purposes it is to be devoted to," he had strong reservations. These he expressed in a four-page letter to J. B. Mac Mullen, board member of the association who was planning to publish the plans in his San Diego *Union*:

Personally, I should have preferred a design which would have permitted us to put up a part of the structure for immediate use at no great cost, so that, later, additions could be made in such a way as to cause the whole building to present an attractive and creditable architectural appearance ... I believe that it would be difficult to, at this time, raise enough money by public contribution to build and complete such a structure as we should have in the end. Most of the present money for this institution comes from three or four people ... We all know that the scale of expenses of a household, or a business institution, is largely fixed by the size and style of that domicile. It seems to me that the going expenses of a concern housed in such a building as proposed would be manifold larger than the annual expense of the Institution at present ... My first feeling on seeing the plans was that of disappointment. It seemed to me that the scheme was developing a degree of impracticability from a business point of view.
(Nov. 23, 1904)

This did not mean that Scripps did not hope that the institution would someday be housed in such a building, or in even larger, more well-equipped facilities. But it was his belief, which he repeatedly expressed, that the station should start out small, that the important thing in the beginning should be men and their work, not material assets.

At the time the plans were presented the building site had not even been finally selected. During the 1904 summer session Ritter, his staff and advisors had come to the conclusion that La Jolla, then a small village fourteen miles north of San Diego, though legally a part of the city, afforded the most advantageous seaside location. But the association was still negotiating with city officials for a plot of land in the city park on Alligator Head near the La Jolla Cove. Until a desirable site was definitely leased or deeded to the association there was no point in planning a permanent stone or cement structure. Ritter promptly concurred. "The plan ... was intended to show as nearly as possible what would be desirable, and to serve as a basis for further consideration," he wrote to Baker soon after the controversy began. "I understood all along that there might very well be a decided discrepancy between what the laboratory *should* be and what it *could* be, at the outset at least."[7]

So a simple plan for a small frame building was drawn up by San Diego architects Hebbard and Gill, with the help of Professor Kofoid and other association members, and in April of 1905 bids were taken. The city council had by this time granted permission for the association to use a portion of the park on Alligator Head, and indeed the La Jolla Improvement Society raised almost all of the $1000 it took to construct the first laboratory designed expressly for the uses of the Marine Biological Institution.

*   *   *

Ritter, Baker, Scripps—all those connected with the research station—must have felt they had seized hold of a many-headed Hydra in the shape of the Marine Biological Institution. There were problems all along the way, countless small matters to attend to with each major decision, inevitable errors in judgment and execution to be corrected. The signing of leases and the paying of bills were indeed part of a world in which Baker and Ritter were not at home, and E. W. Scripps would have had little idea what to do with the material the *Loma* dredged up. None of these people were prisoners of minutiae, however, and the fact that they kept resolutely pushing their plans forward, despite setbacks, indicates that there was a great amount of common ground. Essentially this was the belief they shared in the wealth of benefits science could bring to mankind; more specifically it was their conviction that the institution stood to make a unique contribution in exploring an almost unknown realm.

The guiding beliefs and over-all methods that were to be the mark of the survey are best set forth in the early years in *A General*

Statement of the Ideas and Present Aims of the Marine Biological Association of San Diego, written by Ritter as the introduction to the first volume of publications on the San Diego work, and re-issued as a pamphlet in April, 1905. There is no better way to recapture the spirit of the undertaking than to read Ritter's own words on the subject:

The Idea of a Marine Biological Survey

The investigations on the coast of Southern California now having been in progress for several years, and their continuance being assured for a few more years at least, it seems fitting that this first volume of results should be introduced by some statement of the general ideas animating the undertaking, and of the efforts being made, and means available to realize these ideas. *Investigations in marine biology, intensive rather than extensive in character* ... is the keynote of the idea. An immediate consequence of the adoption of such an idea as a rule of action, has been the necessity of making a clear distinction between *marine biology*, and *general biology prosecuted by researches on marine organisms* ...

The aim as formulated in the articles of incorporation of the Association is, "To make a Biological Survey of the waters of the Pacific adjacent to the Coast of Southern California." ...

The Area to be Surveyed

The funds available being small, an important and everpresent practical question is that of fixing limits. One of the first of these was that of limiting the territory to be surveyed ...

It is, of course, not to be supposed that a stone wall has been built around this area ... nothing is clearer than that complete knowledge of it is impossible without extending the explorations widely beyond it. That it makes a well defined base of operations is about the view we take of it.

The qualifications of the region are: a position well to the south; a considerable extent of continental shelf, presenting a large diversity of bottom, with numerous islands and shoals; proximity to oceanic depths and other truly oceanic conditions; a favorable climate; a large variety of shore line; and accessibility through sea ports and railroads ... A fundamental element in investigations of the sort contemplated is *continuousness* of the field work. Data gathering must go on throughout the year at frequent intervals. The weather here offers little obstacle to this ...

La Jolla, the suburb of San Diego at which the laboratory is located, is on a rocky point jutting into the open sea with water of 200 fathoms attainable inside of five miles; so the ecological problems of oceanic plankton, and of bottom-forms can be here attacked under peculiarly favorable conditions ...

There can be no doubt that deep sea and longshore investigations have not yet been brought together to the extent they ought to be.

The Initial Step

The first step in such a survey would obviously be to find out what plants and animals inhabit the area; to establish a speaking aquaintance, as one may say, with the organisms that are later to be more intimately known. So far this has absorbed most of the effort, and it will of necessity demand the continuance of much effort for a long time in the future ... The entire fauna and flora must be recorded in such a way as to make the records a good foundation for the broader and deeper studies to follow.

Order of Advance on the Numerous Lines of Investigation

A natural sequence, within certain limits, will establish an order ... For example, the species representing a given pelagic group having been got well in hand, a natural second step would be the determination of the seasonal distribution of the group, since the study of the collections for the taxonomy would surely bring together, incidentally, considerable data on this problem. Following close upon the treatment of seasonal distribution would come that of horizontal and vertical distribution, the chorology; and inseparably linked with these would be the problems of food and reproduction; and these would lead again to problems of migration, with their intimate dependence upon temperature and other environmental factors. And here, completeness of knowledge being ever the watchword, the demand would arise for applying experimental and statistical methods in the effort to get at the deeper significance of the facts observed, and generalizations reached from the observational investigations. The chain of questions hanging one to another is endless and, of course, completeness of knowledge in a literal sense, is an unattainable ideal.

Knowledge of the Physical Conditions of the Area

It does not need to be said, in the light of general biological conceptions reigning in this day, that an aim at comprehensiveness of knowledge cannot for a moment neglect the physical conditions under which organisms live ... Conditions of the water as to temperature, and currents; mineral, gaseous, and albuminoid content, etc., must be known at *the particular time and place to which the biological studies pertain*, and no general knowledge of this character can suffice. Physics, chemistry, and hydrography must, therefore, be integral parts of such a survey.

Instrumentalities for Prosecuting such a Survey

It is obvious that no small outlay of money would be essential for even a good beginning; and that considerable progress in it could be made only with large expenditures for both equipment and operation ...

Necessity of a Salaried Staff

Obviously, there must be coordinated effort of numerous special investigators to make any headway. How is this to be secured? In only one way: *by paying for it*. The diversity of talent and training called for, and the prolonged period of service requisite, preclude the possibility of success on any other basis ... the only way by which such a survey can be carried on with any considerable measure of success is through an *organized, salaried staff*. This, of course, means a large and continuous expenditure ... fortunately lessened by the circumstance that while the staff in the aggregate would be rather large, only a portion, and in the main a comparatively small portion, of the time of each member would be demanded ...

Remarks on the Present Status of Marine Biology in General

Situated as our station is, on a biologically almost unknown part of a little known ocean, our first concern, chronologically, must be with local conditions and problems ... we yet venture to look somewhat beyond these limits ... Looking over the whole domain, one sees that while certain geographical regions ... have been cultivated, intensely even, in certain particulars, when attention is directed to large problems rather than to space areas, the thoroughly subjugated portions are exceedingly small ...

... When viewing this whole field of knowledge, and the means and methods of investigation, one must be struck by the prevailing uniformity and inadequacy of the existing marine stations for coping with the situation ... They have been and are, with few exceptions, primarily resorts for individual investigators of specific biological problems, and not for systematically attacking the problems of marine biology proper.

I would wish to guard myself without fail against being understood as passing adverse criticism upon these laboratories ... No other instrumentality has contributed so largely to the promotion of general biology ...

[33]

We are becoming ever more impressed as knowledge advances, with the truth that no segment of the phenomena presented by an animal, morphological or physiological, is fully understood until it is regarded in the light of the entire life career of that animal. We are likewise in a position to see as never before what must be done to attain this fullness of knowledge. We must, in the first place, learn by observation all the facts of the life history of the animal. In the second place, we must make use at every point possible of a combination of observation and experimentation for the interpretation of these facts . . .

We must learn, through careful and extended *observation of the animals in nature*, just what it is we have to interpret. Need for a kind of marine biological research not specially felt a few years ago is now becoming urgent . . .

The portions of Nature unsubjugated by science are vast—it almost seems as though they grow vaster the longer we work at them; and one of the great questions science has ever before her is that of making such effort as she is able to put forth count for the most. One way of doing this is by giving good heed, not alone to the talents and tastes of workers, and money endowments, but as well to the *opportunities* held out by Nature herself.

The conditions placed by Nature before us mark unmistakably the road we ought to take.

CHAPTER IV

THE LITTLE GREEN
LABORATORY AT THE COVE

"THE LITTLE GREEN LABORATORY AT THE COVE," which was to house the work of the biological survey for the next few years, was on the whole a welcome addition to the somewhat barren La Jolla landscape. Acton and Company erected the basic wood structure for $992, and all but thirty-four dollars of this sum was provided by the La Jolla Improvement Society. The generous interest of this group, which represented a community of about 1300 people, had been largely aroused through the efforts of Fred Baker.

Dr. Fred addressed an evening meeting of the society in March of 1905, impressing on his audience of approximately fifty men, women and children the immediate and potential worth of the proposed laboratory, and added that if La Jolla didn't want the station, "we will give grounds and house too quick at Roseville." Three hundred and twenty-five dollars was collected on the spot. The remainder, mainly in amounts of five to twenty dollars, was raised in the next few weeks with the help of Rev. J. L. Pearson of the La Jolla Union Church (Appendix C).

In view of the strain which had been placed on the scientists' relationship with E. W. Scripps during the winter, it was fortunate that new sources of income were found that spring of 1905. Although the laboratory building itself was assured by the La Jolla subscriptions, there was still no provision for the glass tanks and display cases of the museum-aquarium, which was to be the main public attraction. Eventually the requisite amount was scraped together from an assortment of individuals and from businesses interested in promoting La Jolla. Even Miss Virginia Scripps, who admitted she was "more interested in this than the scientific side," gave $300 for museum glassware.

Perhaps the most notable contribution came from Alexander Agassiz, the eminent Harvard-based biologist who has been called "the father of modern oceanography." Learning of the station from C. A. Kofoid, who was a member of Agassiz's six-month South Sea Expedition of 1904-1905, the noted scientist paid San Diego a visit in March of 1905. Agassiz talked with E. W. Scripps and other members of the association at Miramar Ranch, looked over the La Jolla site, and promised substantial support. He gave books and scientific apparatus worth $1500 to $2000, as well as an immeasurable boost to the morale of everyone concerned.

At the request of Baker, who appealed to him as "the most practical man amongst us," Kofoid came to La Jolla in April to supervise the building of the laboratory. Baker himself was reluctant to take on this responsibility so soon after the fiasco of the *Loma*'s refitting, convinced that E. W. Scripps probably thought he "hadn't the business ability to build a chicken coop."[1] Once permission to use the land had been granted the work went quickly, and the modest wood structure was ready for use when the rest of the Berkeley contingent arrived in mid-June. Though small and simple, it was, in the words of Dr. Ritter, "far superior to any residence the station had before occupied."

Measuring sixty by twenty-four feet over-all, the building contained three laboratories of equal size, a small library and still smaller reagent room, and an aquarium-museum for the public. For the first time there was an abundant supply of both salt and fresh water.

Living conditions were more of a problem in the dusty village of La Jolla than they had been in thriving Coronado. In a letter discussing summer plans Baker, who regretfully expressed his view that it would not be possible to board in La Jolla for less than $6 a week, suggested that the men bring sleeping bags and offered to do what he could about a "mess tent." The single ladies were to be lodged in a two-bedroom cottage for which the monthly rent was $22.50. Since some of the assistant researchers were being paid only $40 a month, and several not connected with the university were paying their own expenses, the cost of living was a serious consideration. Nothing was more serious than the work at hand, however, and with the added advantages of piped-in sea water, steadier microscopes and a greater wealth of material due to the *Loma* and her more efficient collecting apparatus, there was much work to be done.

Situated as they were in a public park, with a public bathhouse a few hundred feet away, the researchers became something of a local attraction during the next few summers. On weekends San Diegans came to La Jolla by the San Diego, Pacific Beach and La Jolla Railway to picnic at the celebrated Cove, visit the Caves, and view the fishes in bottles at the "Biological." Shells and preserved forms of sea life lined the walls of the museum-aquarium. Live specimens displayed on a long counter in the center of the room were in open containers supplied with aerated sea water from above, and reportedly were so attractive to tourists that they were sometimes slipped into pocket or picnic basket and carried off. Meanwhile the dedicated scientists and students worked in the adjoining rooms. Several times during the summer there were "Public Days," when the laboratories were opened to visitors, the staff arranged "displays of unusual interest" and "devoted themselves to the instruction of their guests."

Community support was important to the future plans of the Marine Biological Institution, and beyond this, Ritter and his associates sincerely believed that scientists should communicate as much of their knowledge as possible to the general public. Thus the occasional lectures that Ritter, Kofoid and others had given in the San Diego area in previous years developed into a weekly series in 1905. Members of the regular staff and visiting scientists gave popular talks and response was encouraging.

Ellen Browning Scripps, a year-round La Jolla resident now sixty-nine years old, was drawn in along with the rest of the community. She attended many of the lectures and began to take more and more interest in the project to which she had made such sizable contributions on her brother E. W.'s initial recommendation. Although she had faithfully attended directors' meetings and had taken her official responsibilities seriously, it was not until the station moved to La Jolla that she became committed to establishing the institution on an unquestionably permanent basis. In January of 1906 she quietly informed the other directors that she had decided to place $50,000 at the disposal of the association. The exact date at which the gift would be made was for the time being left indefinite, although Miss Scripps and her brother stated that possibly it would come as a bequest at the time of her death.

The announcement of the $50,000 gift came shortly before Dr. Ritter departed for the Orient on his sabbatical leave, and it was decided to make no plans for the money until his return. As 1906 was the last of the three years of work which had been guaranteed by the original $4500 annual subscriptions. There would be ample funds to conduct the regular summer session, Ritter planned to represent the university and the association at an oceanographic congress in Marseilles after visiting Japan and other parts of Asia, and was eager to tell the world-wide meeting of scientists of the ambitious survey they had begun. With the work's continuation guaranteed by the substantial endowment from Miss Scripps, his words would carry even greater weight and promise.

The pledge of $50,000 from a private source also reassured the administration of the state university. President Wheeler and Judge McKinley, chairman of the regents' committee on the institution, paid a visit to La Jolla in late January of 1906 and discussed the endowment and future plans with Miss Scripps and other members of the association. They indicated their continued interest and willingness to cooperate, and in making the official visit strengthened the institution's ties with the University of California, but again refused to make any commitments for the future. In fact the final sentence of the resolution which the board of regents passed thanking Miss Scripps for the endowment set forth the strong reservation that "the acceptance of such trust does not carry with it any obligation on the part of the University of California to provide any funds for any purpose in connection with said work."[2]

Meanwhile C. A. Kofoid, who was to direct the work of 1906 in Dr. Ritter's absence, was busily making plans for the summer session. He corresponded with a number of eastern scientists in the hope of inducing them to spend at least part of the summer in La Jolla, for the association was anxious to bring its work to the attention of scientists throughout the nation. Once the favorable conditions for marine biological research offered by the La Jolla location were recognized, it was felt, some of the most able men in the field would come to pursue their special lines of investigation. Not only would the station become better known through such contacts, it would also benefit from the findings of these men working within the scope of the survey.

Thus in 1906 Professors E. L. Mark of Harvard University, E. B. Wilson of Columbia University, and H. S. Jennings of Johns Hopkins University spent several weeks at the association's expense in the laboratory, and departed as enthusiastic advocates of the location and plans of the Marine Biological Institution. E. W. Scripps interviewed the three scientists at Miramar and reported: "I was informed by these gentlemen that this location of the institute was so desirable—the climatic conditions so agreeable . . . and so favorable to marine investigation—that there was no doubt but that when the institute was finally existing, it would become the Mecca of most American scientists and many foreign visitors."[3]

To furnish these eminent investigators and the regular staff with material for their studies the *Loma* made daily collections. In 1905 the renovated schooner had made a lengthy voyage to San Clemente Island where her ability to dredge at a depth of 700 fathoms had been "conclusively proven." Staying closer to shore in 1906 she was used in hydrographic explorations of the Soledad Submerged Valley off the La Jolla coast and in collecting plankton in water up to 400 fathoms in depth.

All went well until the evening of July 25, when the work at sea came to an abrupt halt. On the trip from La Jolla to the San Diego harbor, when trying to save time by running inside the kelp beds that skirt the coast, Cabral and his crew ran the *Loma* aground near the lighthouse on Point Loma. The boat was caught by the breakers and carried up onto the rocky ledge that juts out from the point.

When attempts to secure the release of the vessel with tugs proved of no avail, the scientists and lab assistants joined with Cabral and his two man crew in a desperate effort to salvage the equipment. Everything of value on the boat that could be removed—including the engines, sails, rigging, and even the copper sheathing and four tons of lead from the keel—was transported almost a hundred yards over the slippery reef and hoisted up a thirty-foot cliff. With the ship listing more and more the hastily-assembled salvage crew barely took time for a few hours sleep and a 2:00 A.M. breakfast at Dr. Fred's home in nearby Roseville. But the next day, when they could pry loose nothing more, they were forced to abandon the *Loma* to her fate.

Thus after less than two seasons of work the *Loma* ended her services as a collecting vessel. The accident must have been a great disappointment to those who had expended so much time, money and mental anguish in preparing her for the job. Fred Baker dreaded telling E. W. Scripps, who had officially deeded the former yacht to the association earlier in the summer, but E. W. received the news of the loss with impressive matter-of-factness. "Well," he is reported to have said, "at least it will kill all those damn fleas."[4]

Perhaps Ellen Scripps already had plans to make her gift before the next summer's work; in any case the wreck of the *Loma* prompted her to quick action. On July 30 she sent an official letter to those concerned announcing that the $50,000 would be transferred to a special biological institute account as of September 1, 1906. As the oceanographic conference in Marseilles had been indefinitely postponed, Ritter was expected to return in August and would be able to help make decisions concerning the expenditure of the money. The most pressing need, of course, was a new boat, and the association's members had learned from experience that they must plan far ahead. In her July 30 letter Miss Scripps gave her full consent to the use of a portion of the endowment for this purpose: "The loss of the *Loma* necessitates the purchase of, or building of, another boat to take its place. I think that this boat should be built especially for the purposes of the association, and that, if practicable, it should be ordered in time to be completed for next year's summer session."[5]

In addition to the usual problems of communication and the necessity of sending plans back and forth between San Diego and Berkeley for approval, there was an understandable reluctance on the part of Baker and Ritter to make the numerous decisions involved in ordering a new boat. Though both had had considerable experience with ships and sailing, neither was an expert, and they were forced to rely on the advice of others in selecting the type and size of boat, the make and horsepower of engine, that would best serve their needs. So it was not until March of 1907 that an $8650.00 contract was signed with San Diego shipbuilder Lawrence Jensen, and twin 25-horsepower engines to cost $2600 were ordered from the Howard Iron Works. By this time it was doubtful whether the new boat would be available for any portion of the 1907 summer session. This was one reason why no eastern scientists were invited to work at the laboratory that year.

The main reason, however, for limiting the research staff to those already involved in the survey, plus a few visiting scientists from nearby institutions, was inadequate space in the building near the Cove. "When it became obvious that the little green laboratory building would have to do for the summer's work," said Ritter in a

1907 article in *Science*,[6] "consideration of the sardine-like condition of things that would be inevitable among the workers, strongly disfavored the alluring of strangers into the pack." Now that funds were available for the expansion of the work there had to be a corresponding expansion of facilities. However there was, as usual, no easy solution to the problem.

As early as November, 1905, questions had arisen concerning the location in the La Jolla park on Alligator Head, when a Mrs. Carey was granted permission by the San Diego City Council to build a sewer that would empty into the La Jolla Cove. Learning of the council's action Fred Baker asked San Diego Mayor John L. Sehon to delay his approval and hurriedly informed Ritter. "One sewer for three houses might not do too much damage," he noted, "but if this is allowed, others could also be granted and the bay contaminated ... I think it safe to say that the emptying of sewage north of Alligator Head would, in time, spoil the only bathing beach at La Jolla and kill one of its chief attractions."[7]

Ritter was, as Baker had anticipated, greatly disturbed at the news. Before leaving on his trip to Asia Ritter wrote a lengthy letter to Mayor Sehon and the council on the subject:

La Jolla was selected for the site of this laboratory after careful study of numerous other possible places on the California coast. One of the weightiest considerations in favor of this as against other points was the fact that here the best of ocean water would be at the very door of the laboratory. The dread of all institutions of this kind is the bacteria that are inevitable in waters contaminated by sewage, as those of land-locked bays and harbors on which cities are situated are sure to be. Obviously, then, were the waters in the vicinity of the laboratory to become polluted by sewage, one of the foremost advantages of the location would be gone.[8]

E. W. Scripps, who had been extremely busy with his newspaper interests during most of 1905 and 1906, took time to add his own strong protest as time wore on and no action had been taken on the sewage problem. "Owing to conditions existing in La Jolla and the high price of lands there, I have been advising the persons interested that it may be well to consider some other location for the building. An offer has been made to the society of another location and substantial inducements."[9] Mayor Sehon assured him that the city was looking into the matter, and had delayed in hopes of finding a less expensive system of sewage disposal than that first proposed by the city engineer. "I know nothing about the La Jolla sewerage subject as a relative municipal economic policy ..." Scripps responded tersely. "The professional gentlemen interested in the Institute have simply informed me that it would be useless to erect a laboratory at La Jolla if the present sewerage system was to continue."[10]

The offer with "substantial inducements" alluded to by Scripps and also mentioned by Ritter in his letters was a very real and earnest one, and came at a most opportune time. Representatives of The South Coast Land Company, with head offices in Los Angeles, were most anxious to have the station located at Del Mar, a budding seashore settlement about ten miles north of La Jolla. These land speculators were convinced that the respectable university-affiliated institution, with its museum-aquarium, would attract a particularly desirable group of people to Del Mar, and they were willing to make generous concessions to obtain it. They offered a forty-acre tract of land, a wharf, a supply of salt and fresh water, a sewer and septic tank, and electric lights.

Awaiting developments in the La Jolla situation, with its problem of water contamination and the further complication of obtaining a title to the Alligator Head location, the association gave no definite answer to the South Coast Land Company for a number of months. They made clear the fact, however, that the La Jolla site was preferred if the problems which had arisen could be cleared up. The Del Mar offer had come while Ritter was on his trip to the Orient, and shortly after his return he wrote to H. W. Heller, president of the company:

I would not have either you or the San Diego people get the impression that we desire to pit Del Mar against La Jolla for the purpose of seeing from which place we can get more. La Jolla is by nature the more favorable place for the station, and my voice will be in favor of remaining there provided the right conditions can be assured. The condition of first importance is pure water; that of second importance concerns the ground itself on which the laboratory would stand; that of third importance is proximity to collecting grounds and to San Diego Bay. In this last Del Mar is distinctly at a disadvantage, and this would be the deciding factor with me were there equality between the two places as regards the first and second points. But as between La Jolla

[42]

with water contaminated by sewage, and Del Mar with water not so contaminated, I should be for Del Mar.[11]

E. W. Scripps also wrote to Heller, holding out little hope that the station would go to Del Mar and basing the preference for La Jolla on the opinions of the three eastern scientists he had interviewed. Professors Mark, Jennings and Wilson, he explained, favored the La Jolla site because of the proximity of rich collecting grounds and the fact that visiting scientists could live more cheaply at La Jolla than "in a place such as you intend to make of Del Mar—a rather aristocratic and high-toned resort."[12] The visiting scientists had taken an active role in the sewage controversy. On a special Saturday "Open Day," for which the railroad had provided free transportation, they had joined Acting Director Kofoid in addressing an audience of 250 on the relationship between sewage disposal and the work of the station. A second set of lectures, for which 800 invitations were issued, was held in San Diego's Unity Hall, bringing more pressure to bear on the city council.

The South Coast Land Company was, nonetheless, willing to wait on the chance that the La Jolla problems would not be solved, and their offer made an extremely useful lever in the association's attempts to pry the city officials out of their lethargy.

The problem of obtaining a title to the land, which perhaps met with less opposition because it was primarily a legal rather than a fiscal matter, was nevertheless a complicated one. The permanent laboratory contemplated by the association would cover nearly an acre of ground when it was completed, and it was thus necessary to secure the entire five-acre La Jolla park if there was to be any room for expansion. This property was held by the city in trust for the citizens of San Diego. City attorneys decided that an act of the state legislature would be required to authorize transfer of the title of the land to the Regents of the University of California for the purposes of the Marine Biological Association. It would also be necessary to obtain by consent or purchase the reversionary rights of the three original donors of the tract.

The unraveling of this tangle of red tape proved to be a time-consuming process, despite the cooperation of state and local officials. The Enabling Act, introduced by San Diego Assemblyman W. F. Ludington, cleared the California assembly and senate in January of 1907, and was signed by the governor on February 7. It was then necessary for the San Diego City Council to make the official transfer in accordance with the act, and this was accomplished in late March. The Enabling Act, Assembly Bill No. 141, provided that the land was to be used by the University of California only for the purposes of a biological station, and should it not be used for this purpose, it would automatically revert to the city of San Diego as a public park. The rights of the public to continued access to the land, biological station or not, were written into the bill:

And further provided: that the public shall notwithstanding any such conveyance, still be entitled to the use of said premises as a public park, excepting so far as such last mentioned is inconsistent with their use as a biological station: That no other buildings shall be placed on said premises than the biological station proper, and that during usual visiting hours the public shall not be excluded from any building or part thereof, excepting the laboratory.[13]

The biological station was now assured a permanent location, and the association began in earnest to plan a permanent laboratory building. Since the city of San Diego had by this time appropriated the funds to furnish La Jolla with a satisfactory sewage disposal system, the path seemed to be cleared of obstacles. But before the sigh of relief had died away, the other members of the association became aware that E. W. Scripps was starting off in another direction and they would have to run to catch up with him.

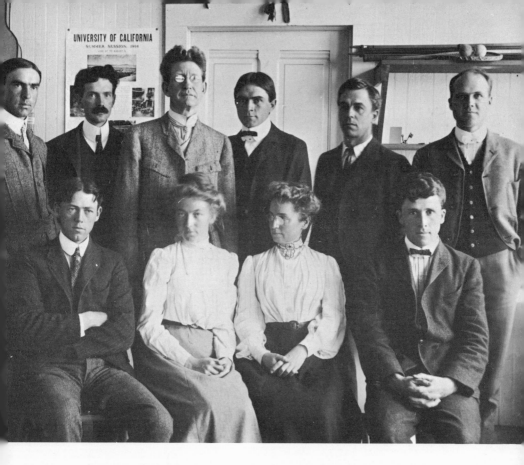

Staff and students of the Marine Biological Station at Coronado, 1904. Seated left to right: John F. Bovard, Effie Rigden Michener, Alice Robertson, Calvin O. Esterly. Standing: Robert Day Williams, B. D. Billinghurst, William E. Ritter, Loye H. Miller, Charles A. Kofoid and Harry Beal Torrey.

A part of the "village" of La Jolla overlooking the Cove with the Marine Biological Association's "little green laboratory" in the foreground. La Jollans donated the $992 it cost to build the laboratory, which was first used in the summer of 1905.

Director William E. Ritter, 1903-1923.

Dr. Fred Baker, San Diego physician, naturalist, and civic leader, who first invited Ritter to bring his biological studies to San Diego served as President of the Marine Biological Association for all but one year before the station was transferred to the University of California in 1912.

Edward Wyllis Scripps, instrumental in involving his sister, provided valuable support and guidance throughout the institution's early years and continued to help make important decisions until his death in 1926.

Miss Ellen Browning Scripps, who early was drawn into the activities of the Marine Biological Station, became its main source of financial support. An officer of the institution both before and after its transfer to the University of California, Miss Scripps helped to formulate policy and made possible many of the institution's scientific advances. She is pictured here in her La Jolla home, 1927.

The ALEXANDER AGASSIZ *was built for the Marine Biological Station and launched in August, 1907, at San Diego.*

The tiny building in the far distance, left, is the first Scripps hall on the barren pueblo lot of 170 acres, sold for $1000 to the Marine Biological Association by the City of San Diego.

George H. Scripps building just completed in 1910, still in use in 1966.

Dr. and Mrs. Ritter at home on the top floor of the George H. Scripps Building which, as the first building at the station, doubled as laboratory and residence.

The Scripps Building, (center left, above) became the nucleus of a complex of buildings which by 1916 included the museum library (joined to the Scripps Building by a bridge), the aquarium (behind the two larger buildings above), the pier, the Director's home (on the triangle of land, above right) and housing for visitors and staff scattered over the hillside.

Thomas Wayland Vaughan, Director from 1924-1936, took great pride in his grounds and is pictured here in front of the library in the spring of 1934.

(Photograph courtesy of Carolyn Vaughan Fortune)

August 30, 1936. Back row, left to right: D. L. Fox, W. E. Allen, G. F. McEwen, James Ross, Richard Fleming, Roger Revelle, Martin Johnston, E. G. Moberg, F. B. Sumner. Front row: C. E. ZoBell, P. S. Barnhart, Easter Cupp, Tillie Genter, T. Wayland Vaughan, Ruth Ragan, Ruth McKitrick, S. W. Chambers, and Snooks.

Director Harald U. Sverdrup, 1936-1948.

This romantic sailing ship was purchased in 1937, renamed the "E. W. Scripps" and made the first of the institution's long expeditions. The ship survived in the fleet until 1955 and then was used for the movie "Around the World in Eighty Days." It now rests at the bottom of the Papeete Harbor.

First long cruise of the E. W. SCRIPPS *into the Gulf of California in February,* 1939. *This picture is part of the group aboard at sea north of Cedros Island. Left to right: Erik Moberg, Roger Revelle, Seaman Andrew Boffinger, Richard Fleming (with binoculars), Machinist Bob MacDonald, UCLA Botanist George Hale, UCLA Botanist Lee Haines, Engineer Walter Robinson, Martin Johnson, UCLA Ornithologist Loye H. Miller. Not in the photograph, Captain Earl Hammond, Anthropolgist Harry Allen, José and Ernest Roque. Director Harald Sverdrup joined the group at Guaymas.*

Scripps Institution of Oceanography in 1938, before World War II.

Director Carl Eckart, 1948-1950.

(Photograph courtesy of Navy Electronics Laboratory)

These new ships, left to right Horizon, Paolina T, *and the* Crest *were added to the fleet in 1948.*

July, 1950—The HORIZON *steams off on operation Mid-Pacific, first of the institution's major exploratory expeditions, carried on jointly with Navy Electronics Laboratory and with a scientific staff recruited from several institutions. Mid-Pac logged 15,368 miles and marked a new era in oceanographic research.*

On board ship during operation "Mid-Pac": Roger Revelle, leader of the expedition, left, Robert Dietz, Edwin Hamilton, Kenneth Emery, Robert Dill and others examine a dredge haul of rocks brought up from the mid-Pacific mountains, an undersea range southwest of the Hawaiian Islands, which was discovered on this expedition.

Scripps Institution of Oceanography in 1952. The Thomas Wayland Vaughan Aquarium Museum Building is on the right.

Roger Revelle, Director, 1951-1965, receiving the Albatross Award in 1954 from Professor Hans Pettersson, famous Swedish oceanographer.

These new additions to Scripps Institution of Oceanography by 1959 show the huge post-war development of the Institution. At this time the fleet numbers seven ships and long expeditions of the Institution's ships around the world totalled 439,988 miles.

Fred Spiess (right), acting Director 1961-1963, Director 1964-1965, is talking with Donald Wilkie, Curator of the Thomas Wayland Vaughan Aquarium-Museum.

FLIP, Floating Instrument Platform is returning to the horizontal. When in the vertical position she displays only 55 feet of her total 355-foot length. FLIP has no motive power of her own, is towed to station.

William A. Nierenberg, who became Director in 1965.

Scripps Institution of Oceanography in 1966 with Revelle College in the distance. Scripps is now part of the University of California San Diego campus.

The newest research vessel, ALPHA HELIX, *is shown here at the dedication cere-
monies of the Scripps Marine Facility, the* ALPHA HELIX *and the* THOMAS WASHING-
TON *on March 11, 1966. This new ship is an ocean-going laboratory that provides
a modern fully equipped biological station for work in any part of the world.*

Chart track of the exploration by ships of the Scripps Institution of Oceanography 1950-mid 1965.

(Courtesy of Dr. Robert L. Fisher)

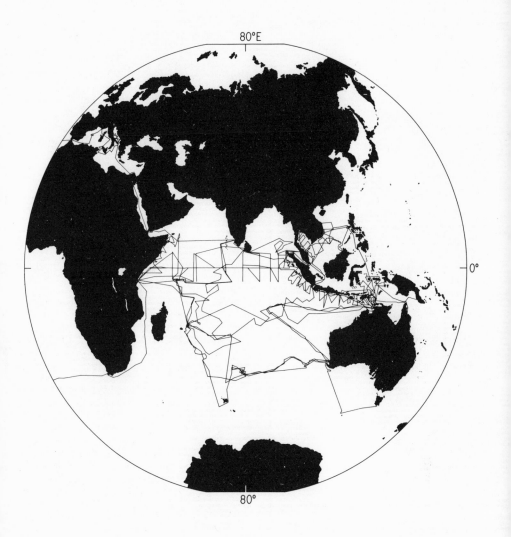

William E. Ritter Hall on the right and Harald U. Sverdrup Hall in the back-ground, 1966.

CHAPTER V

UNDER THE HAMMER

Since the very beginning of the controversy over the La Jolla park site, E. W. Scripps had from time to time expressed a view that the association should seriously consider other locations. It was against his independent and practical nature to have to ask and wait for favors from the public and its representatives; he would have preferred to buy up the best available tract of land and start building. "However, there are others far more deeply interested in the project than I," he admitted to Mayor Sehon. "The University itself is a public institution and must, of necessity, consult the wishes of large bodies of tax paying citizens."[1] In the same letter, then, he went on to present arguments toward procuring the desired La Jolla park. During the long period of uncertainty about obtaining the Alligator Head land, however, his initial impatience was tempered by sincere doubts concerning the adequacy of the five-acre tract to accommodate the growing institution. By the end of 1906 he had come to the conclusion that a larger building site must be obtained. His sister Ellen was among the first to be brought to his way of thinking. "I am so accustomed in almost all matters of discussion between us to his larger, new, deeper insight and surer foresight that I generally become a convert to his views despite my own opinions or prejudices,"[2] she wrote Baker soon after the city passed the ordinance transferring the park to the association.

"This is rather disconcerting at this stage of the game,"[3] wrote Mrs. Ritter from Berkeley, summing up her husband's reaction as well as her own. So much time and energy had gone into clearing up the problems of contaminated water and gaining a clear title to the park land that everyone concerned was reluctant to suddenly relinquish what they had won. But this was not an idle whim on E. W.'s part; he advanced strong arguments to back up his view. Gradually persuaded that they might indeed find the park site "inadequate for their future growth, and objectional because of the prohibitive stipulations in the deed of gift and also because of the inevitable growth and rush and enforced environments of La Jolla,"[4] the members of the association had begun to look for a location without such limitations. Their search soon confirmed their suspicion that the only suitable and available land in the vicinity was a pueblo tract of indeterminate size lying beyond the Long Beach, about two miles north of the La Jolla settlement. They had earlier discovered that there was uncertainty not only about the size of the tract but also about its ownership.

Cause of the confusion was a seventy-one-year-old San Diego man who claimed to own all of the land along the coast from La Jolla to Del Mar. He had broadcast this claim so widely that Baker and Ritter were informed that he owned the desired tract; they wrote him and made arrangements to talk with him. He seemed to be in complete sympathy with their plans, offering to give them as much land as they needed. "In my opinion he is insane," wrote Baker after one interview. "He says that all of his titles are in other names—a common insane delusion—but can be put in his name in fifteen minutes . . . for fear we may be entertaining an angel unawares I will try to follow him up a little further."[5]

Ritter and E. W. Scripps also visited the would-be donor during the summer of 1907, and even had the San Diego city attorney check the validity of the eccentric's claim. It finally became clear that the tract north of Long Beach, Pueblo Lot 1298, was owned by the city and contained approximately 170 acres. "You could have had my deed to the said 40 acres, or to the whole of Pueblo Lot 1298 more than a month ago," wrote the self-appointed, now disappointed, public benefactor. "But now since you have had it published that the City owned Pueblo Lot 1298 and requested the City to put it up at Auction the only thing left for me to do is to deed 1298 to the City instead of deeding it to the Marine Biological Association. And then if Mr. Scripps wants to buy what he could have had for nothing that is his affair . . ."[6]

Mr. Scripps and the association did want to buy Pueblo Lot 1298, and it now became their task to persuade the city to sell it to them on reasonable terms. The leap from negotiating for five acres to trying to buy 170 needed some explanation. Ritter gave a public lecture on the subject in July of 1907. "The chief patrons now have larger ideas and purposes for the future of the institution than they had in the beginning—than they had a year ago, in fact," he told his audience. " ... the directors are at one with the patrons in recognizing the importance of a much larger station site." He went on to emphasize the desirability of a La Jolla site, described Pueblo Lot 1298, and noted that it could be obtained only through public auction. "It is hoped—it is confidently believed, in fact—that, the purposes for which the land is to be used and the character of the transaction being generally and fully understood, the Association will be the only bidder, and so will be able to purchase the tract at a relatively low price."[7]

Ritter outlined some rather general uses the station might have for so large a tract of land, but E. W. Scripps in his businesslike way drew up a list of specific plans and proposals which in *his* view (presented to the city council in behalf of the association) made 170 acres almost essential. He stated that the association planned to "immediately erect a permanent structure costing $20,000, this structure to be in such form and shape as will make it eventually only a part of a much larger structure ..." Then the association would "almost immediately erect" cottages for residential and part-time staff, and after these, cottages for the use of visiting scientists. This took care of forty acres. Scripps went on to say that "it is expected in time to establish on these grounds" botanical gardens, a museum of natural history, and "something in the nature of what is commonly called a zo-ological garden." There seemed to be no limit as to what the institution might become:

It should be understood by the public that the work of this Association is not to be limited to the establishment of a branch station of the University, the sole aim and object of which is to confine its efforts to only one branch of biological science. It is the desire and intention to erect on this foundation a school or even a college of biological research, its field of operations to embrace a very large part of the science of biology.

The Association believes that it has reasonable grounds upon which to base expectations of obtaining such large financial contributions from the National Government, from the State, from large and endowed educational institutions, and from private parties, as will insure for the future a full development of its plans and even the possible extension or enlargement of the same.[8]

Evidently no one brought forward reasons that were anywhere near as good for *not* selling the land, so Pueblo Lot 1298 was put up for auction on August 10, 1907. The sale was duly announced in the August 9 San Diego *Union*:

WILL SELL CITY LOT SATURDAY

Clerk Butler to Dispose of Land for Biological Station.

Guesses are being made as to what the property will bring under the hammer. One estimate is $10 an acre . . .

And duly reported on Sunday, August 11, the day afterward: -

So far as outward appearances went the auction sale of Pueblo Lot 1298, La Jolla, from the G Street steps of the city hall yesterday forenoon was a quiet affair.

City Clerk Butler officiated. The work was done in less than five minutes although ample time was given for all necessary details.

The only bid was by Harry L. Titus, Vice-President and General Counsel for the Marine Biological Association of San Diego and was for $1000.

The sale was declared made to the Association and Julius Wangenheim, Treasurer and one of the Directors, promptly produced two one hundred dollar bills, the percentage of the purchase price demanded by the conditions of the sale, which money was turned over to Mr. Butler.

Not more than a dozen people were present, four of whom were real estate men. The bid of Mr. Titus, however, was evidently more than anyone cared to raise."

Considering the value of the land involved, estimated to be between $30,000 and $50,000 at that time, the association had found quite a bargain. The $1000 was not the city's only compensation, however, The La Jolla park once again became city property, and the value of the centrally-located five acres was probably greater than that of the outlying and barren pueblo tract. In addition to this, in the event the association obtained the land, Miss Ellen Scripps had promised to provide $10,000 for a road from La Jolla through the tract to the Torrey Pines near Del Mar. In the deed of sale a strip of land 100 feet wide was reserved to the city for this boulevard, and work upon it was begun immediately (Appendix D). Somewhat straightened today, this road, as La Jolla Shores Drive, wound for many years along the hilly coastline of north La Jolla, and was the main route north from San Diego to Los Angeles. A further consideration in the sale had been the fact that E. W. Scripps, on behalf of his sister and himself, had intimated that they were prepared to give as much as $200,000 toward the further development of the biological work at La Jolla.

The Marine Biological Institution had thus at last obtained a permanent home. It could not have been described as "homey." Only ten of the 170 acres were level land on the ocean front; the remainder consisted of "barren brown hills, canyons and arroyos," bounded by sheer cliffs along the sea. Even when the new road was built the site was still isolated from the La Jolla settlement and its conveniences. But the spirits of the association's members were not dampened by the seeming desolation. E. W. Scripps at once offered to donate seedlings of eucalyptus and other plants of the hardy varieties he had found to flourish on the sea coast, and began to explore the possibilities of piping water to the site at an early date. In November, 1908, he reported the success of his efforts to Ritter:

The Mayor . . . and I have evolved a plan of planting to eucalyptus and other trees a large part of the city land lying up north of the Biological land . . . I want the nursery to be at some handy spot, probably on the Biological land . . . they must hurry up the Board of Works to get the pipe in, at least as far as the biological station, immediately. They have all promised to attend to this matter on the instant . . . in a short time we will get a nursery started for the city in which we can also raise all the trees we want for our own biological land planting.

Unquestionably there were definite advantages to the location which out-weighed its temporary inconveniences. The problem of water contamination would never arise, there was room for almost unlimited expansion, even the isolation would for a time insure undisturbed scientific investigation free from the press of a curious public.

Meanwhile, with visitors wandering into the museum-aquarium daily, the work of the survey was going steadily on at the Cove laboratory. In 1907, despite the fact that no eastern scientists were invited to La Jolla, a paid staff of thirteen plus seven "accommodated workers" crowded into the small building. Although the new boat was still under construction, means were found to provide researchers with ample material with which to pursue their studies.

That summer Ritter summed up the results of the work at San Diego, now in its fifth year, for a brief article in *Science*:

Some 518 kinds of organisms have been studied critically so far as the needs of identification and records are concerned. Of this number 106 have been described as new species. It is fair to assert, I believe, that as a result of these four years' work, some at least of the animal groups inhabiting our waters are better known to science than are the same groups of the Atlantic shores of the United States, where marine laboratories have existed and marine collecting has been practiced for forty years at least."

If Ritter was encouraged in 1907, he had even more reason to be so in 1908, for by this time the new boat was ready to do any sort of at-sea work required by the investigations on plankton within the area marked off for the survey. Of the five names suggested, Miss Scripps had favored the *Alexander Agassiz*, and thus the ship was to be christened at her scheduled launching on August 16, 1907. A large crowd assembled on that day only to find that the event had been postponed. When the *Agassiz* finally was launched on August 21 she ingloriously stuck in the sand at the water's edge and had to be pulled into the water by a launch. Fortunately the first set of engines had been taken on approval, and when these proved unsatisfactory in numerous tests late in 1907, they were taken out without cost and replaced in the spring of 1908 with twin Standard Engines of thirty horsepower each. The *Alexander Agassiz*, a modified scow, was eighty-five feet long over-all with twenty-six foot beam, forty tons register, and had been built and outfitted for a total cost of about $16,000. After the intensive 1908 collecting season, when she had proven to roll too much in rough water and when problems had become apparent in the arrangement of her collecting apparatus, certain modifications were made. Her mainmast was shortened and made lighter, her steering gear was transferred from aft forward, and a wheelhouse, chartroom and naturalist's house were added to her facilities.

Despite imperfections, the *Agassiz* was by far the best boat the station had yet had for collecting and, though she cost almost $25 a day to operate, yielded results that were well worth the expenditure. Her size necessitated a crew of five, and, as there were sleeping accommodations for nine, a galley and ample storage space on board, longer trips were now possible. "I have laid out a big hard summer's work for her," Ritter wrote to Kofoid, who was in Europe that summer of 1908, "including a line of soundings and serial temperatures and water samples from north Coronado Island to Cortes Bank, with an anchorage on the bank if possible for current determination, and a run 200 or 300 miles to the south and west in search of a northerly set of water."[9] In connection with this work George F. McEwen, an instructor in physics from Stanford University, joined the regular staff. "The particular satisfaction in having a physical laboratory operating in conjunction with the biological work," wrote Ritter in a 1908 article in *Science*, "lies in the fact that whenever a special biological question comes along requiring information from the physical side, the physicist can be appealed to *then and there* ... an advantage quite apart from that of having on hand a general stock, so to speak, of information about the water such as the systematic work of the physicist puts into the records."[10]

The work of sounding, measuring temperatures and many aspects of the collecting would be facilitated in 1909 with the improved equipment for these purposes which Kofoid was shipping from Europe. Visiting marine biological stations on his sabbatical leave, Kofoid had been especially charged with studying the facilities and operations of laboratories at Liverpool, Bergen, Naples and elsewhere in view of their applicability to the permanent laboratory to be built at San Diego, and the association had contributed a small sum toward his expenses. He soon discovered that the finest scientific instruments could be bought at a great saving in Europe, and wrote, as the association's superintendent of equipment, asking for an appropriation of funds with which to purchase the new and better apparatus he had found. Eventually he was granted a total of $800 for the purpose.

Kofoid's letters were read with great interest by Ritter and the other directors, for they were anxious to incorporate his findings into the new laboratory for which designs were being completed. "We shall, I think, begin on the new laboratory the moment we have reports from you that will enable us to do the best that has been done so far in piping, particularly," Ritter wrote him in June of 1908. "Hope you will give special attention to this. La Jolla is badly torn up and very dirty from street and park improvements. We are all now anxious to get away to our own ranch."

Construction of the new building at the "ranch" did not actually get underway until the following spring, although funds for the permanent laboratory had been available for almost three years by that time. There had been numerous causes for delay, including the extension of a road and a water line to the site, but the greatest obstacle had been disagreement among the directors of the association themselves.

Treasurer Wangenheim, who had been appointed Chairman of the Building Committee at a September, 1906 meeting of the association, favored San Diego architects Hebberd and Gill, who had designed his own home. Evidently Irving Gill, whom Wangenheim respected for his sense of line and architectural harmony, had a reputation for paying no heed to costs in making up his designs. When he showed signs of living up to that reputation the other directors became alarmed. "The building that we sketched out, you will remember, I got estimated cost of from an experienced contractor here in Berkeley," Ritter pointed out to Wangenheim in early 1907. "He assured me that it should be built for about $25,000. Hebberd and Gill calculated that the same building out of the same material would cost $48,000."[11] At talk of withdrawing the plans from Hebberd and Gill, Wangenheim offered to quit his post as building committee chairman, which had become, in his opinion, an "empty honor."

Everyone entered into the fray. Wangenheim talked with Miss Ellen Scripps, who could see no objection to Hebberd and Gill. E. W. Scripps referred to Gill as "one of those kind of men ... who could make a very fine design that would only be useful providing there was plenty of money on hand to meet any cost,"[12] and in Berkeley Ritter dealt as judiciously as he could with the opposing views which reached him from San Diego. Eventually the situation righted itself; Wangenheim agreed to guarantee on his own every penny over the estimates that Hebberd and Gill's plans might cost them, and the designs were finished. The first set of plans had been drawn before the actual building location had become final, and had to be redrawn for the new site. There had also been a lengthy discussion of building material, during which stucco, concrete block, and brick were gradually eliminated in favor of reinforced concrete. But finally, in January and February of 1909, bids were taken, and a wholly new cause for concern arose.

The building committee's estimates for constructing the building as planned had ranged around $20,000, with $25,000 set as an outside limit. When the bids for the excavation and concrete work came in, two of them were near $12,000, and one of them was for only $6400. There was understandable hesitation about accepting the low bid, for it meant that the two-story structure would be built for less than $13,000, and this scarcely seemed possible without recourse to inferior materials or workmanship. If the bid were accepted, the directors agreed, the work would have to be carefully supervised by a representative of the association.

The low bid was taken, and Perl Acton and Company, who had also built the laboratory at the Cove, agreed to do the carpenter work as well as the excavation and concrete work for a total of $9700. Signed on March 24, 1909, the contract specified that work was to begin on or before April 1 and be completed by October 1, 1909, barring unavoidable delays. A variety of smaller contracts were let for such jobs as plumbing, electrical work, lathing and plastering, and the construction of aquariums. Although Ritter planned to arrive soon enough in the summer to oversee all but the preliminary work of excavation and laying of foundations, the association also hired a construction superintendent. For the first time in the organization's young life, money was the least of its worries.

In 1903, when Ritter had estimated that $500 would support the first summer's work in San Diego, he could not have foreseen that within five years the station would have, as it did, an annual income of $6000. In addition, the Marine Biological Association by the end of 1908 had assets of approximately $70,000, including the library painstakingly assembled by H. B. Torrey, scientific equipment, the *Alexander Agassiz*, the land north of Long Beach and the $32,000 cash balance of Miss Scripps' endowment. As forecast at the time of the auction of Pueblo Lot 1298, E. W. and Ellen Scripps were prepared to go even further. On February 25, 1909, Miss Scripps added a codicil to her will which read, in part:

I give and bequeath to the Regents of the University of California, the sum of $150,000 for the work of the Marine Biological Station to be carried on at or near La Jolla, California, on the following conditions: (1) That, during the effective years of his life, the work of the station shall be carried on in accordance with the biological ideas of Professor W. E. Ritter, so far as this is consonant with the general policy of the University; (2) That he shall be the Scientific Director of the station at a salary of not less than $3,000 a year, and shall not be removable, except for cause; (3) That there shall first be conveyed to the Regents of the University of California all the property, rights and privileges owned by the Marine Biological Association of San Diego . . .[13]

Miss Scripps also changed other sections of her will to provide that should certain of her beneficiaries die before she did, the cash legacies designated for them would go to the work of the station.

The bequest was made with the major stipulation, implicit in the codicil, that Ritter should take up his residence in La Jolla and direct the work on a continuous basis. This idea had figured prominently in one of E. W.'s earlier letters to Ritter:

I am confident that, could you have been able to devote your whole time to this institution, you would have before this got it well started and far better endowed . . . I am afraid valuable time and opportunities have been lost by reason of our not having an effective organization, and permanent and continuous work.[14]

Thus when the Ritters arrived in La Jolla in June of 1909, it was to establish a permanent residence in the dusty little town. Not all ties with Berkeley and the campus with which they had so long been associated were even formally severed. Dr. Ritter was still to receive one-third of his salary directly from the university, two-thirds being provided by the association, and he was to spend a month or two each year giving a short course of lectures in Berkeley. By far the major portion of his time, however, would now be devoted to the Marine Biological Institution of San Diego. Ritter had been willing to draw his entire salary from the association, but again E. W. Scripps had advanced a strong opinion on the matter:

For various reasons, among others perhaps, my own knowledge of myself, I am led to believe that for every dollar the University itself invests in this work, either in paying you part of your salary and furnishing you equipments, or in any other way contributing to the work, there will eventually be several dollars more added to the fund. My sister and myself will, I know, unconsciously perhaps, be greatly influenced in what we do by the interest evidenced in the work on the part of the University . . .[15]

The summer of 1909, then, was a notable one in the life of the biological institution. It saw a continuation, for the fifth consecutive year, of the research work in the little green laboratory near the Cove, and it marked the beginning of a new era. The Ritters settled temporarily into a comfortable house on the cliffs above the La Jolla caves, from which they could just make out the lonely concrete structure going up at the far end of the long, flat beach north of the town. As soon as it was feasible they would move to that isolated setting and try to make there a home, a research institution, and a lasting contribution to human welfare.

CHAPTER VI

THE REGENTS AND THE RANCH

"A SURVEY OF THE WATERS of the Pacific adjacent to the coast of Southern California"—what an enormous task Ritter had laid out for the Marine Biological Institution. The deeper the researchers delved, as he had predicted, the more questions they came up with. Now that a few links of knowledge had been forged, Ritter and his associates were becoming more and more aware that it was indeed an "endless chain" of questions, which they had just begun to answer. The survey would take perseverance. In 1911, ten years after it had begun on a steady, organized basis, Ritter was to write of the work:

> The natural and inevitable expansiveness of such an undertaking will be seen by any one who has even a meagre acquaintance with the phenomena to be investigated and the methods that must be employed. The farther one advances in experience and knowledge, the more does he become impressed with the vast scale on which things are done in the ocean and the literally infinite complexity of cause and law there in operation. Except for the gleams of light that early promise more light and the fascination there is in overcoming difficulties one might welcome a pretext for turning back, once he has gone far enough in such an enterprise to see what is actually on his hands. Mere enthusiasm is too evanescent, and initial personal ambition has too many alternatives to hold one steady on such a course.[1]

Nor was the "infinite complexity" limited to the realm of scientific investigation. Seemingly endless, too, were the problems which arose with building the laboratory, maintaining a boat, finding the staff to carry out the arduous investigations and, most important and least certain at times, financing the enterprise as a whole. Now that he had taken up his residence in La Jolla, Ritter was even less free to devote himself to his own research. As "the man on the ground" he was now largely responsible for the mass of petty details which over the years had been handled by various members of the association. It seemed that nothing was ever accomplished easily.

The building on the new site, which was scheduled to be completed by October 1, 1909, was not finished until mid-1910, due to the inevitable "unavoidable delays." One of these was the shortage of gravel, for which crushed rock had to be substituted at an additional cost of $800. Even when the basic structure was erected the plumbing and electrical work were yet to be done, as were numerous other jobs of finishing and the installation of special scientific features. The large concrete water tank, found to leak when it was filled, had to be emptied and coated with waterproof material. To further complicate matters, it was necessary to clear this and other unexpected expenditures with the board of directors of the association, as well as with Miss Scripps' attorney, J. C. Harper, who from Cincinnati had charge of disbursing the $50,000 endowment which provided both the building fund and part of the operating expenses for the current work of the survey. Thus the problem of communication among those with varying degrees of responsibility was still a serious consideration.

Meanwhile, there was much to be done to make the large tract of arid land of the new location somewhat less barren and inhospitable. During the winter of 1909 and in 1910 Mrs. Ritter, in "a stout Stanhope trap," oversaw the planting of thousands of eucalyptus seedlings which were to enhance both the beauty and the value of the land. Unfortunately, many of these died in the unusually dry winter of 1909, but enough survived to form the basis of substantial groves of these trees in later years. Ornamental shrubs were planted around the building site itself, and gradually the land took on a less forlorn aspect, so that "the ranch" began to look more and more attractive to the handful of permanent staff members awaiting the day when they could move from their cramped quarters near the Cove to their new home.

Even the work of landscaping was not without its problems. The cattle from an adjoining ranch broke through their inadequate fence many times and trampled the young eucalyptus trees. "Of late the cattle have been entering our building and have become such a nuisance about the premises that it would be necessary to have them kept off our land even were we not going to plant the trees," wrote an exasperated Ritter to the owner of the cattle in November, 1909.[2]

He was still sending letters in 1912: "I was up on the mesa yesterday and find that since I was there a few days ago your cattle have broken and badly injured some thirty or forty of our trees."[3]

Despite numerous setbacks the location north of Long Beach was gradually taking on the appearance of a biological station, but even this fact was not met with enthusiasm from all quarters. "Every time I pass over the road leading by the new building of the Biological Station," wrote E. W. Scripps in June of 1910, "I see, in this building, a sign board pointing out the road to nowhere that I would care to go."[4] The previous summer E. W. had dictated a long tract entitled "The Biological Station Begins to be a Disappointment," and had sent copies of the twelve-page document to Ritter and to his sister Ellen. The chief cause of his disillusionment was his feeling that the building chosen to house the work at this point was ostentatious and unnecessarily luxurious. "The planned laboratory of the Biological Station is in my opinion as useful for its ostensible purpose as would be a grindstone worn around the neck of a man to protect his throat."[5] He expressed his disappointment in Ritter as "the workman who, if not complaining of his tools, holds an altogether too high a regard for these inanimate instruments," and restated his view that the best things started small: "Simplicity and great work are absolutely necessary companions."

The letter of June, 1910, was a much more serious matter, however. "The financial scale that has been set, for the institution, is one that will involve more capital than I could afford, or than I could properly advise my sister to invest, even though her interest and mine, in the undertaking, were as great as it is small," he wrote. "I think it is fair to you to state that I will counsel my sister to add nothing to her previous contributions to this work."[6] In July, when E. W. was again elected to the board of directors of the association, he declined to serve.

At the same time, however, Attorney J. C. Harper was informing Ritter of the arrangements Ellen Scripps had made to provide the necessary funds for the fiscal year ending July, 1911, and included in the total amount was E. W.'s usual pledge of $1500. "The foregoing provision is limited expressly to the coming year and no pledge or promise is made or is to be inferred as to the future," Harper added.[7] Nevertheless, with finances assured for another year, Ritter and his staff could proceed with the work at hand and hope that the tense situation would be eased during the year. Ritter evidently did not look on Scripps' letter and resignation as signs of a permanent break between the station and its chief patrons. "Mr. Scripps, you may know, does not accept his election to the Board of Directors this time," he wrote Vice-President Titus, "so we shall have to find someone to take his place."[8]

During the summer of 1910, not long after Ritter returned from Berkeley after giving the first of his short courses of instruction there, the new building was ready for occupancy. As the laboratory had, whether wisely or not, been constructed with future expansion in mind, all of the current scientific work could be contained on the ground floor, which consisted of six individual workrooms, a large aquarium room, a shop, storage room and janitor's quarters. This left the second floor free for use as a temporary director's residence. To Mrs. Ritter fell the task of transforming the six small laboratories, the library, apparatus room and enormous lecture hall of this second floor into the semblance of a home—a task to which she was evidently quite equal. Outside of the rectangular, two-story cement building, the only other structures on the grounds were the water tower, a tool shed and garage. Before the main entrance, which faced west, stretched the usually sunlit expanse of the Pacific, broken by the curve of Point La Jolla on the south and bordered by an irregular wall of cliffs to the north. Isolated though it was for the time being, the biological station's new home had ample scenic compensations.

For the next few years the residential staff was necessarily small, and the major part of the laboratory investigations still were carried on during the summer. The meagre funds of the institution were so arranged, however, even in 1910, to provide salaries for Ritter as director, Ellis L. Michael and Myrtle Johnson as full-time scientific assistants, John Dahl as master of the *Alexander Agassiz*, Nina Waddell as part-time librarian and a superintendent of the grounds. Also receiving some compensation for their part-time work were Professors Kofoid and Torrey of the University of California, C. M. Child of the University of Chicago, C. O. Esterly of Occidental College, and G. F. McEwen and H. C. Burbidge of Stanford University.

Miss Johnson and Edna Watson, a former student of Dr. Ritter who was helping him on a special project, lived in one of the laboratory-bedrooms on the second floor of the biological building, as the two miles to La Jolla was deemed too great a distance for the young ladies to have to traverse twice daily. E. L. Michael, who had been the station's resident naturalist for several years prior to Ritter's move to La Jolla, lived with his family in the village and had to commute by bicycle or foot over the dusty road. When spells of rainy weather came to La Jolla the journey was scarcely worth it. "Experience has taught me that when I travel the two miles through the rain," wrote Michael in March, 1911 to Ritter, who was recuperating from a serious illness in drier inland towns, "by the time I get a fire built to dry my clothes and thaw myself into a decent humor for intelligent work it is then nearly time to go home again."[9]

The case of pneumonia with severe complications which had brought Ritter near death the previous winter kept him from giving his spring lecture course at Berkeley in 1911, as his doctors had ordered a long convalescence. But by the time the work of the summer began in June, Ritter was back in La Jolla to direct the survey and to write a long tract on the station and its work entitled, "The Marine Biological Station of San Diego—Its History, Present Conditions, Achievements and Aims," as well as a short yearly report for publication in *Science*.

In his *Science* article on the summer's work, Ritter noted that the most important biological event of the year was the final issuance of E. L. Michael's "Classification and Vertical Distribution of the Chaetognatha of the San Diego Region." This not only recorded and described the species of these transparent worms so far taken in the area, but also dealt quantitatively with the large amount of data which Michael had collected from 1904 to 1909. The continuous study of this group in its environment yielded some of the first results of the Marine Biological Institution's work commensurate with its specific methods and goals, and was considered of great significance by those connected with the survey. Also published this summer were the fourth and fifth numbers of Kofoid's "Dinoflagellata of the San Diego Region." C. O. Esterly had by this time accumulated a great deal of information on the copepods of the region, including their seasonal and vertical distribution, and Ritter and Michael were pursuing similar studies on the salps. In addition to extending the same investigations of distribution and movements to other pelagic animals, it was hoped to complete the salt water supply system for the laboratories and landing facilities for boats within a year or two, so that the same groups might be subjected to laboratory experimentation.

Although the hydrographic investigations which McEwen and Burbidge of Stanford were carrying on were held to be "primarily in the interest of biological problems," Ritter noted that some of the results being reached were "of themselves so important as to make them closely rival in interest the biological work itself." McEwen had mainly devoted himself thus far to testing Ekman's theory of oceanic circulation as it applied to the phenomena of upwelling waters along the continental margins, while Burbidge was perfecting methods of measuring the gaseous contents of the water. Both of these studies yielded valuable information bearing directly on the current biological investigations of distribution and migration.

Another interesting development of the summer of 1911 was that the institution made arrangements with the California State Game and Fish Commission for the study of the "spiny lobster," and with the Bureau of Soils of the U. S. Department of Agriculture for estimating the quantity of kelp along the coast of Southern California for such industrial purposes as might be found for this plant. Although research in pure science was still to be the primary object of the station, Ritter explained, "Whenever, as in these cases, it happens that equipment and experience can be made to serve industrial ends without considerable interference with research, the management is more than glad to thus extend the station's usefulness." Dr. B. M. Allen of the University of Wisconsin was in charge of the inquiry into the lobster fishery, while the kelp studies were carried on under the direction of W. C. Crandall, an instructor in biology at the San Diego State Normal School, who at this point was both Secretary of the Marine Biological Association and Captain of the *Alexander Agassiz*.

Thus with a combination of year-round and seasonal staff the San Diego Marine Biological Institution was making great headway, although ideally, in Ritter's view, it would require a minimum permanent staff of eleven to carry out the projected survey most efficiently. Such an increase in personnel, however, could be made only with a sizable increase in income, and those most involved in the station were thus anxious to find additional sources of revenue.

This was the main reason why Ritter spent a large part of his time in 1911 writing "The Marine Biological Station of San Diego—Its History, Present Conditions, Achievements and Aims"; for although the Association knew they had something of value, the long exposition was needed to make that value clear to others. Foremost among those they were trying to interest were the Regents of the University of California. In some ways the interest of this body in the enterprise had been evidenced throughout the years, but several members of the Association felt that the University had not done all it could to make clear its support or to contribute materially. "Sometime ago, several years ago, in fact," wrote E. W. Scripps in November of 1911, "it appeared to me that the University, so far from desiring to have the institution, seemed to feel that we were in a position of trying to get something out of them."[10]

Earlier in the fall of 1911 Ritter and Kofoid had advanced to President Wheeler and the regents the idea of transferring the affairs and property of the institution to the university at that time, and had met with a cautious response. "The results attendant upon the acceptance of the Lick Observatory with its annual heavy charge upon the general funds will effectively stop the acceptance of a conditional gift of the La Jolla enterprise," wrote Kofoid to Ritter, "if the conditions involve present or prospective expenditures from the university funds other than those now made in the way of publication and library facilities."[11]

As it had long been planned to eventually make the biological station a part of the university, Ritter, Kofoid and some of the other directors continued to push matters toward that end. E. W. Scripps came forth with alternative proposals, and even suggested that they see if the Carnegie Institution in Washington, D. C., might be willing to adopt the station. Less than a year after his "resignation" from the board of directors, E. W. was back taking an active part in the station's affairs. "From the fact that Ellen has without advising with me on the subject given Mr. Harper full instructions I judge that I have now been relegated to second or even third place in the institution. From such a position I feel that it would be pleasant rather than otherwise to contribute some attention and some money," he wrote Ritter in February, 1911.

In November E. W. wrote a long letter to Albert Schoonover, legal counsel for the Marine Biological Association, which read in part:

The fact of the matter is the University does not seem to be interested in the biological station as an institution of learning. It is only now that the institution represents actual property in money values, to several hundred thousand dollars extent, that they consent to give it any consid-eration whatever. It is the money that they will be looking after, and not the educational opportunities.

I have no fault to find with the University, or the Regents, and I harbor no resentment against them . . . I feel certain that for the present, at least, the University would only be a bad stepmother to the institution if we allowed it to be adopted by it . . .

As the present association is an unfit instrument and as the University is not yet ready to take hold of the institution and give it much better service, I have proposed as possibly a temporary expedient the formation of a new association to take over the property and to inherit certain bequests . . .

As things stand now, but very slight additional cost on us would be entailed, if the station were to be entirely separated from the University. One thousand dollars more per year would have to be raised for Pro-fessor Ritter, and we would have to buy some instruments of our own, the cost of which would be comparatively insignificant . . .[12]

Everyone agreed that some kind of new arrangement for the control of the station's finances was absolutely necessary. "Now that the Association owns property each member of the Association has the legal status of a stockholder, so that if the affairs of the Associa-tion were closed up the property could be sold and the proceeds divided," E. W. had pointed out.[13] The Scrippses were naturally reluctant to make any further large contributions to an enterprise with so shaky a financial structure.

As assistant director of the station, C. A. Kofoid, who was now chairman of the zoology department at Berkeley, stated the case to President Wheeler when he returned from meetings with the board of directors in early December, 1911:

1. The donors of the existing property of the station, Miss Ellen B. Scripps and Mr. E. W. Scripps, regard the present Association as insufficiently safeguarded to receive or control any additional endow-ment. 2. They desire that the holding organization be made legally safe, and, for business and personal reasons, wish to retain, until such time as the legacies shall become available, control of the prospective endowment whose income is now paid to the station for its running expenses.

[63]

On the basis of his talks with the directors and previously with Wheeler and V. H. Henderson, Secretary of the Board of Regents, Kofoid went on to make the following recommendations:

1. That the University arrange with the San Diego Marine Biological Association for the formal transfer to the Board of Regents of the University of the existing property of the Station, with such safe-guards as shall protect both the University's interests and the donor's purposes. The property will thus escape impending taxation.

2. That the present management of the affairs of the Geo. H. and Ellen B. Scripps Biological Station be vested by the Regents under such conditions as shall be mutually agreed upon in a local Board of Control . . .

By this time the university officials, after an investigation of the matter, were favorably disposed toward the proposal, and it was now a question of working out the technicalities of the transfer. There was a great exchange of letters in early 1912, and in March Ritter went to Berkeley to give his lecture course and to complete the transaction. It was decided to postpone the actual transfer until the beginning of the University's fiscal year on July 1, so the Marine Biological Association continued in existence for a few more months. By the end of July, however, the papers had been signed.

The Marine Biological Association deeded its real property, "in consideration of the sum of ten dollars ($10.00) and other valuable considerations," to the Regents of the University of California to become a department of the university "co-ordinate with its already existing departments." This property was to be used "exclusively for the purpose of maintaining, improving and developing the Scripps Institution for Biological Research of the University of California." (Appendix E) E. W. had wanted both his sister Ellen's and his brother George's names to appear in the title of the institution, but in the end only the Scripps surname was retained.

The relationship between the university and the station was clearly defined in the Constitution and By-Laws of the Local Board of the Scripps Institution for Biological Research, to which the preamble read:

All property, real and personal, together with all rights, franchises and interests of any kind whatsoever, pertaining to the Scripps Institution for Biological Research, are vested in the Regents of the University of California, a corporation, subject to the agreement with the Marine

[64]

Biological Association of San Diego, that the local control of the property, and business and scientific policy shall be vested in a Local Board of Directors.

Consisting of the governor of the state, the president of the university and certain regents; the scientists currently on the staff of the institution; E. W. and Ellen Scripps, J. C. Harper, Fred Baker and "such other lay members as may contribute a sum not less than $10,000"; this local board retained almost full responsibility for the affairs of the institution. The regents would have the final word on the appointment of the director and business manager and would retain certain "powers and jurisdiction" over the property of the institution, but otherwise matters of scientific policy, the hiring of personnel, receiving and disbursing of funds were left in the hands of the local board. For practical purposes the powers of the board could be exercised by an executive committee consisting of the president of the local board (an office filled by the director of the Scripps Institution) and two other directors.

In the agreement which the regents made with the Marine Biological Association prior to the transfer it had been stipulated that the control of the institution by the local board would continue "during the lifetime of Miss Ellen B. Scripps and until the final settlement of her estate," and that during this period the regents and officers of the university would "use their best efforts to secure the largest possible state appropriations to promote the work of the station." This agreement also restated that the official designation of the station would be "The Scripps Institution for Biological Research of the University of California," understood to be a memorial to Miss Scripps' deceased brother, George H. Scripps, from whose estate much of the endowment had been derived.

In his official report to the President in 1912, Ritter had this to say of the institution's change in name:

One may hope that the dropping of the word 'marine' from the name will not be taken to mean that a relinquishment or even curtailment of researches at sea is contemplated. The reason for the change was that those chiefly responsible for the enterprise, whether as financial supporters or essential custodians, had become fully convinced that biology in the largest sense ought to be the aim of this particular foundation. It is not to be supposed that anyone connected with the institution contemplates researches in the whole range of sciences of organic being, particularly at any one time. It is believed, however, that an endowed institution with no specified limit of duration, ought to have the utmost freedom as to the particular provinces of the vast domain of biology that it should cultivate at different periods of its existence."

This wider view of the institution's future was in complete accord with Ritter's personal interest in scientific philosophy. It was his feeling that the investigations should in no way be limited if there was a possibility of their adding something to the higher knowledge of mankind. In a section of the long memoir written in 1911 which he titled "The Duties to the Public of Research Institutions in Pure Science," Ritter went into the subject thoroughly:

. . . an institution of research in biology or in astronomy could justify its existence, in a democratic country like ours, only by making considerable additions to knowledge and then by showing, in language comprehensible to the generally but non-technically educated members of the community, something of the meaning of this knowledge for human beings in both the physical and spiritual aspects of their natures.

One might have thought, reading Ritter's grand statements of purpose, that the institution he spoke of had almost unlimited staff and financial resources. In reality there were very few people working full-time in the lonely concrete laboratory that was yet too large for their needs. But Ritter was even more certain in 1912, with the institution officially a part of the University of California, that it would grow into and outgrow these facilities. "One cannot adopt a baby elephant for a pet without sooner or later having a big elephant on his hands, if he treats the creature humanely,"[14] he had once written. But throughout the years he had firmly believed that size alone meant nothing. "If the station does the things I would have it do it will, unfortunately, have to be rather big." he wrote in 1910. "My ambition for it—and in this I am sure that I speak for its patrons and official friends as well as for myself—is that it should be great rather than big."[15]

CHAPTER VII

THE BIOLOGICAL COLONY

ON THE DAY THE TRANSFER of the biological station to the University of California became final—July 12, 1912—Comptroller Merritt sent an official statement of the new institution's needs to Ellen Scripps, noting that the regents had been informed she would be "glad to ... provide the necessary funds for the further expansion of the work." In consultation with Merritt, Ritter had listed the binding of volumes and purchase of new books and journals for the library, the construction of a sea wall and a pier, and the installation of a salt water pumping plant as the most essential of the improvements needed to allow for such expansion. Merritt further informed Miss Scripps that an engineer would soon be sent from the university to make a thorough survey of the institution's land. After completing a detailed map and a careful study of the property, this engineer would draw up a report on the best means for its future development and protection. In carrying out the trust they had accepted, Merritt added, the regents would pledge themselves to act "as fast as funds are received, giving the work careful attention in every detail."[1]

Thus assured that her investment was in safe and competent hands, Ellen Scripps in turn informed the regents and other members of the local board that beginning in July, 1912, she would pay to the regents the sum of $2500 each month for a period of two years—until a total of $60,000 should have been reached. This sum was to be used solely for the physical development of the institution. In addition she and her brother E. W. would continue to make their annual contributions of $9000 and $1500, respectively, for the station's operating expenses.

With expanded facilities those running expenses would necessarily increase, and it was decided in 1912 to make every possible effort to obtain an appropriation from the state legislature. Not long after the California Assembly and Senate convened in early 1913, Dr. Fred

Baker journeyed to Sacramento to present the biological institution's case. Ritter, J. C. Harper and other members of the local board had contacted as many legislators and university officials as possible, and had been advised to ask for appropriations for specific projects, such as the building of the pier, rather than for costs of maintenance. On the basis of this advice Miss Scripps had changed the stipulations on her $60,000 gift to make the larger part of that sum available for operating expenses.

In light of Miss Scripps' generosity and her willingness to accommodate changes in plans, the advisability of making any appeal whatsoever to the state legislature might have been questioned. Certainly the amount requested—$33,600 over a two year period—was small compared with her own previous contributions. However, as J. C. Harper pointed out to Governor Hiram Johnson, Miss Scripps could not go on supporting the institution indefinitely:

> Time is important. The chief donor, Miss Ellen B. Scripps, is over 75 years old. She may not be in the land of the living when the next Legislature meets . . . The importance of action at this Legislature lies in the fact that it will be evidence that the state is really interested in the work that the institution is doing and will foster it after its chief benefactor has passed from earth.[2]

Such evidence of the state's willingness to maintain the Scripps Institution for Biological Research, Harper tried to make clear, would encourage Miss Scripps to make still greater contributions to the enterprise.

Evidently some of these efforts at persuasion were well-placed, for the Scripps Institution did indeed receive a $15,000 appropriation from the 1913 California legislature. Although this was less than half of the amount requested, it added $7500 to the station's income for each of the next two years, allowing for an increase in staff and more frequent and effective use of the *Alexander Agassiz*. In the early weeks of the legislative session it had once more been decided to ask for a portion of the institution's operating expenses, as the request could then be included in the general appropriations bill and would have a much greater chance of renewal—"almost as good as an outright endowment by the state . . ." Comptroller Merritt wrote. "I am of the opinion that it will never be taken away from the institution."[3]

To oversee the expenditure of these various sums of money, Wesley Clarence Crandall joined the institution staff as business manager on February 1, 1913, after several years of part-time association with the station as naturalist, master of the *Alexander Agassiz*, and secretary of the Marine Biological Association. Thus relieved of many administrative details, Ritter was able to spend more time on coordinating the scientific work and pursuing his own studies, while under Crandall's efficient direction the physical plant grew rapidly in the next few years.

H. B. Foster, the university engineer who had spent several weeks at the institution surveying the property and laying out roadways and building sites, had laid the groundwork for a number of the necessary improvements, but priority was given to housing. A few weeks after Crandall took over as business manager he began the building of twelve cottages of various sizes, which were ready for occupancy early in June, 1913, and were soon filled by permanent and summer staff and their families.

These "one-board" houses, which had been built and furnished for about $1000 apiece, were far from luxurious. One occupant noted that "the roofs leaked badly at every pore in the heavy rains, and the wind blew through the cracks."⁴ Mrs. Ritter described them as "truly masculine in their planning and lack of conveniences."⁵ and the bill for furnishings summons up visions of rather bleak interiors, with iron beds at $5.75 each, "sanitary couches" costing $4.00, and burlap curtains throughout. Dr. Ritter, who was still living on the second floor of the laboratory building, viewed the cottages with his usual calm acceptance: "When their cheapness is considered in the light of the clear desire of Mr. Scripps to make as large a portion of the funds as possible available for the main purposes of the institution," he wrote Kofoid, "their simplicity can be accepted with much greater complacency."⁶

One of the next projects which Crandall supervised was the building of a home for Ritter himself, who had practically been evicted by the unfeeling scientific director. The latter explained the situation to Comptroller Merritt in a letter dated August 13, 1913:

"The Scientific Director of this instituition has given the Local Board of Control notice that he must have the upper floor of the laboratory building now occupied by Mr. W. E. Ritter and his family as a residence, for scientific purposes within the next few months, and that consequently unless provision is made for a new domicile for the present occupant, he will shortly be without a home."

Fortunately, quick action was taken, and a new director's residence was constructed by December 1, 1913, on a point of land north of the laboratory. This roomy two-story wood structure, unlike the "temporary" cottages, was regarded as a "permanent improvement," and cost about $4000 to build.

By the end of 1913, then, a little colony was growing up around the main laboratory building of the Scripps Institution for Biological Research. The institution had purchased its first car, a model T Ford, and a garage and several small service and storage buildings were clustered in the immediate vicinity of the laboratory. E. W. Scripps had lent roadbuilding equipment, and well-graded roads and driveways began to provide access to new building sites.

It had been decided to postpone the building of the pier for a year or two, as the estimated cost of erecting one as long and strong as was desirable would practically exhaust the funds designated for improvement. Neither was the selection of a contractor to undertake this rather difficult task a decision to be made hurriedly. In addition, there was still some doubt as to the most advantageous location for the pier.

Meanwhile, a provisional salt water circulatory system was installed, equipped with an electric pump capable of delivering 2100 gallons an hour to the laboratories and aquarium. The intake pipe for the salt water supply eventually would be located at the extreme end of the pier, where clear water might be obtained. For the time being, a temporary intake pipe was run well out from the shoreline, and a settling tank served the double purpose of clearing the water and providing an outdoor aquarium.

Another major improvement in this early period of growth under the university's auspices was the building of a sea wall, 250 feet long and about eight feet high. The embankment in front of the laboratory had been wearing away at an alarming rate, and everyone concerned was considerably relieved once the concrete wall was firmly in place "to stay the inroads of the sea upon the cliff," as Ritter expressed it.[7] To prevent erosion from surface water a drainage system was installed on the more level portions of the institution's land.

By late summer in 1914 bids had been taken on the construction of the pier and the institution was engaged in negotiations with a Los Angeles firm when the outbreak of the war in Europe brought plans to a halt. It was several months before prices of building materials had stabilized and the institution was once again willing to undertake major construction. By this time Miss Scripps had added another $100,000 to her contributions, and the greater part of the $34,000 it would take to build the pier could be drawn from this new improvement fund. The Mercerau Bridge and Construction Company of Los Angeles, who had had experience building other concrete piers on the California coast, contracted to build the wharf, including davits and storeroom, for $26,954. Approximately $7000 more was to be expended on salt water pumping equipment, storage and sedimentation tanks, and a retaining wall.

Miss Scripps' new gift of $100,000, which she and her brother announced in April, 1915, was to be paid in monthly installments of approximately $4200. Unlike the $60,000 given immediately after the transfer of the institution to the regents, this new sum would be handled through the local board rather than the comptroller's office. There were several reasons for this arrangement, which lessened the work of the comptroller and his staff as well as relieving those at the institution charged with requesting, spending and accounting for university-controlled funds. The primary consideration Crandall described as a "psychological" one. This was the desire on the part of E. W. Scripps to see his sister more actively involved in the affairs of the institution. "Mr. Scripps believes it is for the best interests of Miss Scripps health that she have some thing or things doing with which, although not overseeing them, she shall be closely enough in touch to have the sense of accomplishing something," Crandall explained to Comptroller Merritt.[8] Thus to avoid "formalities and red-tape," the Scrippses planned to turn over their proposed additions to the physical plant in finished form, although they readily agreed that the various projects would only be undertaken with the regents' approval. Crandall, in addition to his duties as institution business manager, would act as the Scrippses' agent in completing these improvements.

The contract for the pier was signed on May 6, 1915, and the construction work was soon underway. As the result of observations by the station's staff during the several years of delay before it was built, the pier was placed some 300 feet to the north of the entrance to the laboratory, where "smoother and better water" could be reached by its 1000 foot span. Since it was to be used as a landing place for boats and for obtaining the best possible water supply for the salt water aquaria, these were important considerations.

The piles for the pier, which were made of reinforced concrete, had to be firmly sunk in the bed rock underlying both water and sand. During July, 1915, the workmen found that the depth of water and sand was constantly increasing over the estimates. The institution was faced with a crisis: if more money were not provided to extend the piles to these new depths the pier would have to be considerably shorter than had been planned. With her usual incisive judgment, Miss Scripps urged them to build the pier to its full length, agreeing to pay the extra expense if it could not be made up elsewhere in the budget for improvements.

Already the most costly of the institution's facilities, the wharf and its equipment promised to go well over the $34,000 alloted to it. Being built at the same time however, were three small "temporary" structures which cost altogether only $4000. These were a three-car garage, a service building near the entrance to the wharf, and a public aquarium building—all of which, according to Ritter, would "add greatly to the efficiency of the physical plant."⁹

The little wooden public aquarium, measuring twenty-four by forty-eight feet, was erected just north of the laboratory building, and freed a large area on the first floor of the concrete structure for other purposes. Percy S. Barnhart, who had come to the institution from the Venice, California aquarium in late 1914, was in charge of arranging displays and collecting and caring for the inhabitants of the nineteen cement tanks with plate glass fronts which lined the walls.

Another department of the institution which definitely needed enlarged facilities was the library. Of the $60,000 which Miss Scripps had turned over to the regents in 1912, one-fourth had been alloted to building up the library and binding many of the pamphlets and journals already on hand. Thus a great many additions had been made to the shelves on the second floor of the laboratory building between 1912 and 1916, and the local board was fully aware of the need for more room. In budgeting the $100,000 improvement fund, then, the board allowed $20,000 for a library-museum building.

A newspaper account of the construction of this building in 1916 indicates that in the minds of some of the staff and patrons of the institution, at least, it was only one part of the grand scheme:

The central structure of a group of six buildings to be erected at the biological station at La Jolla is nearing completion and it is hoped it may be finished and ready for occupancy by June 1 . . . The six buildings will be so grouped as to form a capital letter 'E' . . . This building . . . the library and museum . . . is of Italian Renaissance style of architecture . . . and will have terra cotta roof, of Italian tile . . . As the library grows it is planned to use the museum for additional stack room, the museum to be transferred to another building in the group . . . The building, while the central feature of the proposed group, is the second to be erected. It will be connected with the first building—the laboratory—by an artistic bridge with a 30 foot span.[10]

This building, designed by San Diego architects Wheeler and Halley and constructed by the firm of Winter and Nicholson, went up more quickly than the first of the permanent buildings. Although the contract had been let on January 12, 1916, due to floods the work did not get underway until March 1; despite this delay, the work was completed by mid-June. Including excavation and grading, architects' fees and interior furnishings the new library-museum cost almost $25,000.

It had been planned to complete the major additions to the physical plant in time for the Assembly in Science, a non-credit course of instruction for secondary school science teachers and other interested members of the community, which was scheduled to be held at the institution from June 26 to August 5, 1916. This aim was accomplished, and a large hall on the ground floor of the new library-museum was used for the lectures that were a part of this first major effort on the part of the institution to make its findings available to the public. Although response by the general local community was gratifying, only a handful of science teachers and students took part in the sessions. Originally a sizable number of residential students had been expected, and partly for this reason twelve more cottages, most of them larger than those completed in 1913, had been added to the housing facilities. These were built on scenic hillside sites north of the laboratory. At the cliff's edge a $4000 commons building with dining space for forty people, which was to be used for recreational as well as dining purposes, was also constructed in time for the experimental summer school.[11]

Thus during 1915 and 1916 there had been a large number of major and minor additions to the Scripps Institution's facilities, and these were collectively dedicated at an afternoon ceremony on August 9, 1916. A large audience assembled in the new lecture hall to hear the notable speakers who had been invited for the occasion. University President Wheeler presided, introducing David Starr Jordan, Chancellor Emeritus of Stanford University, who spoke on "A Plea for Old-Fashioned Natural History"; D. T. MacDougal, Director of Botanical Research of the Carnegie Institution, who spoke on "Biological Research Institutions: Organization, Men and Methods"; G. H. Parker, Professor of Zoology at Harvard University, who spoke on "The Sources of Nervous Activity"; and W. E. Ritter, whose topic was "What the Scripps Institution is Trying to Do."

Although this dedication drew a large crowd from the local community, none of the university regents, to whom Ritter had sent personal invitations, attended the ceremony. In fact, as Ritter pointed out shortly after in a letter to President Wheeler, wherein he set forth the institution's grievances against the university, only two of the regents even acknowledged the invitation. A more serious grievance was Ritter's charge that during 1916 the university had shown no inclination to help the institution secure an appropriation from the state legislature, although it had faithfully presented the requests of all other departments. Fortunately with whatever help it could muster and through its own efforts the Scripps Institution obtained appropriations of $12,500 for each of the years 1915 through 1918, and was able to increase its income from the state to $17,500 in 1919 and 1920.

The Scrippses remained the chief source of income for all purposes during this period, although the percentage of the station's maintenance provided by the state would continue to increase. There were other minor sources of income which, though they brought in a relatively inconsequential amount, made the institution's staff feel a little less dependent. One was the supplying of various specimens of marine life to universities and other biological laboratories, a practice which P. S. Barnhart and his predecessors had begun somewhat informally on their own in response to requests from investigators who knew of the institution's resources. Simple ascidian were only fifty cents a dozen, but Ritter wrote one specimen-seeker that the institution would "have to charge $3.00 a dozen for the big blue jellyfish."[12]

A small monthly income was also derived from the rentals charged for the cottages on the institution's grounds. In 1914 a three-room cottage rented for $12.00 a month and a six-room cottage was $21.00, not including linen or silverware. These rents were cheaper than those charged in the town of La Jolla, and despite the "simplicity" of the accommodations most of those who came to work at the laboratory chose to live on the premises. Another strong factor influencing this decision was the poor condition of the road connecting the station with La Jolla—especially during the rainy season. In early 1916 the rains were so heavy that there were serious floods in the San Diego area and portions of the road to La Jolla were washed out. The mules and muleteers who were currently employed in constructing the pier were put to work building three bridges to re-connect the station with its main source of supplies.

When it was not muddy it was dusty along the two-mile stretch of road, and transportation was always a problem. For a number of years, at least in the summer, the institution provided daily automobile service (5c for regular trips, 25c for special trips) to town, and eventually the local bus service was extended to the station. But for most of the members of the "biological colony" trips to town were rare. The scientists and their families kept largely to themselves in their own little community, where, due to the construction activity, mud and dust were ever present.

Everyone who lived at the institution in this period seems to have been impressed with the dirt. Memoranda concerning each worker's responsibility for cleaning up his own corner were circulated, and wives recall dust-covered groceries and ankle-deep mud along the roads and driveways.[13] When Ritter became acquainted with H. F. Osborn, "the leading paleontologist of this country," at Berkeley and sent him down to visit the institution he hastily wrote Crandall, "Don't let him see our place looking 'down at the heel' and dirty."[14]

Crandall was doing his best to keep the place clean and in good repair, but even the Ritters' house leaked in the heavy rains. "We went up to the house and made things as shipshape as possible using all the linen that could be found to save windows, etc.," Crandall reported after one storm. "The wind whooped it up so I nailed on some additions to your sleeping porch and finally got it so that it didn't leak worth mentioning."[15]

At first the cottages were heated by wood stoves that were none too satisfactory in the wet, cold weather, especially since the wood supply wasn't always kept dry. Although oil burners came to be used, it was some years before electricity was installed in the houses, so the bleak winter evenings were illuminated only by gas lights. Mrs. Ritter, who later referred to this period as one of "pioneering in a biological institution," saw to it that bushes and trees were planted around the cottages. She also maintained a large and productive vegetable garden, setting an example that many of the other wives soon followed.

Growing a portion of their own food needs was not only an economical move on the part of the members of the colony—it was also much less complicated than relying on local merchants for everything. Dairy products and eggs were available from a farmer who lived on the hilly, eastern section of the institution's land,[16] but other supplies had to be ordered from town. A grocer was eventually found who would take orders and deliver to the institution, and for a while Crandall kept track of orders and collected individual grocery bills along with his other duties as business manager. Although payment was made easier with the opening of individual charge accounts, certain inconveniences were retained in the system. For some years all the grocery orders were left in the hall of the laboratory building, where they were vulnerable to the raids of a marauding desert tortoise, a colony pet, until some member of the family could carry them to the proper cottage.

The institution was considered to be out in the country in these years before La Jolla had expanded beyond its village bounds, and various forms of wildlife were plentiful. At one time everyone was put to work collecting horned toads for C. A. Kofoid, who needed them for some experiments at Berkeley. As might have been expected, very little hunting was done by this colony of naturalists; those who did have guns contented themselves with firing at tin cans and other such inanimate objects. Ritter even asked that the rattlesnakes, who were fairly frequent visitors, be spared unless killing them was unavoidable.

It was a good life for those who liked the out-of-doors, with ample opportunity for hiking and swimming. In addition, a tennis court had been built soon after the institution had located on "Biology Beach," and it was maintained as a permanent feature of the colony for years. Before and after the commons building was erected there were numerous joint activities among the colony families. Often they all got together for Thanksgiving or Christmas dinners, and beach parties centered around a huge pot of fish or clam chowder were a frequent and popular pastime. Nor was the community spirit limited to good times. Mrs. F. B. Sumner, whose husband joined the staff in 1914, remembers a brush fire that swept down off the mesa during her first year at the colony and threatened many of the homes. The women and children took refuge in the laboratory building while the men stayed up all night fighting the flames. Fortunately the wind direction changed abruptly and all the buildings were spared.

With accommodations for as many as a hundred people on the institution grounds the colony was virtually a separate town in those days. Mrs. Barnhart started an informal little school for the younger children, and for a while her backyard classes included some of the Mexican road crew, who were anxious to learn English. Hoboes who passed along the road between Los Angeles and San Diego used to stop off at the cottages and ask for handouts. Another hazard of having the highway run through the institution property was that occasionally someone's brakes failed on the steep Biological Grade.[17] Early residents can recall several instances when trucks or cars came careening down between the cottages, although some drivers chose to head their runaway vehicles into the bank.

The unique homogeneity of the little community and the fact that it actually was a "planned town" set E. W. Scripps to thinking, and late in 1915 he put these thoughts down in a disquisition entitled, "An Odd Place: A New Town Where High Thinking and Modest Living Is To Be the Rule." From his brother Fred, E. W. had acquired forty acres of land adjoining the institution on the north and, as he was free to dispose of this property in any way he liked, he envisioned a new kind of real estate venture:

Now, there is being established in the city of San Diego a new sort of subdivision, on which building restrictions are to operate. However, instead of lot owners being required to build a costly house, they are required to build the cheapest and most modest house at all consistent with purely material comforts.

After describing the institution as it then was, with the laboratory, service buildings and first twelve cottages standing, and the pier, library-museum and aquarium building under construction, he sketched in some of the "plans" in mind for the future. A schoolhouse, cooperative store and "clubhouse" were soon to be erected, and "twenty or thirty new cottages" would go up within the year, which would be rented for "a short or long period of time" to the public. Not just any public—"The kind of settlers most desired," E. W. stated, "are those retired professional, literary, and other quiet people who naturally seek association with scientific men." There were ample inducements for those who liked the outdoor life. "The pier will probably be one of the best fishing places on the coast"; he noted, "while the two miles-long beach, to which a rock and concrete road will lead, will be desirable for both promenading and bathing."

If the experiment had gone through it would have constituted one of the first benevolent oligarchies on the California coast. "The governing board of the new town will, if practicable and legally permissable, consist of the local society and directors of the Scripps Biological Institute," E. W. wrote. "The settlement and post office will probably be named Ellentown."

Rental charges on the cottages to be built on the institution's land would be very moderate, E. W. explained, as no one connected with this particular real estate venture was out to make money. He even offered to give the title of an acre lot of his own land to any professor or "other attache" of the institution who desired to build his own home and own his own property, provided the recipient would spend no more than $2500 on his house and would respect these building restrictions:

First—No house will be allowed to be built, either on the biological land or the adjoining property, other than such a structure that even a man with the most modest income could afford to own or rent. In other words, there are to be no fine or even moderately costly homes built in this new town, such as will cause the occupants of humbler homes to feel any sort of inferiority in the matter of financial status.

Second—Even at the expense of much land being withheld from building purposes, no house will be built so that it will obscure the beautiful view of the ocean from the residents of another house.

P. S. Barnhart and F. P. Sumner actually did acquire building lots on the basis of this proposal, and Scripps loaned each of them the money to build their houses.[18] The money repaid on these loans was to go to the institution for special needs. E. W. also spent $1,191.56 to extend his scenic cliff road further to the north to give access to these building sites. Various legal problems arose regarding the institution's rights to the lots thus given to individuals if the owners should leave, and the local board placed certain limitations on the two-lot transaction and, unable to find a solution, deferred any further disposition of the forty-acre tract.[19]

So the "odd place" as outlined by E. W. Scripps never came into existence, though the place that did exist had its odd aspects. It is impossible to form a conception of what the Scripps Institution was at this time, however, without knowing something of the people who populated the colony and, more important, of their work.

CHAPTER VIII

OF MEN AND MICE

FRANCIS B. SUMNER, who, after joining the staff in 1913, was to spend more than thirty years of his life at the Scripps Institution, had this to say of the life and work at the "biological colony" in the early years:

One must bear in mind, too, the blighting effects of our isolated life, out there, well outside the limits of La Jolla, particularly before anyone but the director owned a car. Here was a small group of ultraspecialized specialists, dwelling alongside a community of laymen knowing little of our work and caring even less. Save for the director's sympathetic interest in everything that was going on in the laboratory, there was very little real intellectual comradeship among the staff. Despite the theoretical cooperative program in which we were all supposed to be engaged, each of us kept to his own little cubicle and seldom left it. We lacked both the stimulation and the corrective restraint which come from competitive endeavor and intelligent criticism by fellow specialists. Rarely did we visit other centers of learning, even Los Angeles or Berkeley, and rarely did we see scientific guests, except as transients, making us a few hours visit. And so we tended to become more and more introverted, and more and more lacking in perspective.[1]

This is the opinion of only one of those engaged in research at the Scripps Institution in its formative years, and may or may not have been shared by others. It was reflected in the director's annual report to the president of the university as late as 1941, however, when the report stated:

Emphasis has again been placed on attendance at scientific meetings by members of the staff because the isolated location of the Scripps Institution makes it desirable for the staff to retain contacts with other workers in their fields and to establish new contacts.[2]

Certainly there were elements of truth in Sumner's description of the youthful Scripps Institution. For one thing, during the decade following the institution's union with the University of California, the permanent staff remained very small. True, by 1916 there were more than two dozen cottages, ranging in size from three to six rooms, on the institution grounds; but these were used mainly in the summer months, or by off-season visiting investigators, or even by artists and writers and week-end vacationers from San Diego and elsewhere.[3] Only a handful of them housed permanent residents. The La Jolla Journal's weekly column on the institution during this period, entitled "Biological Notes," is filled with brief accounts of who is visiting whom, what visiting scientists are expected, and which of the graduate students or clerical staff is departing. Those few who stayed year-round in the isolated setting must indeed have tended to concentrate on their individual investigations and not depend for intellectual stimulation on the changing stream of summer researchers and visitors.

There is much evidence, however, that the few salaried staff members did cooperate on various projects, were at least informed of each other's work, and made use of one another's procedures and findings in carrying on the survey of the Pacific. Sumner, although his experiments with land-dwelling mammals were held to be "applicable" to the survey, undoubtedly was forced to work in more isolation than those who were involved in the study of the ocean and its life.

The zoological contingent of the permanent staff still dealt primarily with plankton in the institution's early years as part of the University of California. Ritter finished up his own plankton studies in 1913, turning in the remaining years of his administration to problems more directly related to his interest in biological philosophy. He was always available in the afternoons for consultation with his staff members, however, and kept well-informed of their progress.

The zoologist who had been working for the longest period of time on a year-round, continuous basis, was E. L. Michael. As Ritter had pointed out in 1911, the results of Michael's work, in regard to seasonal movements and distribution of the chaetognatha over a period of years, was of great value to the survey. Important information concerning   description and taxonomy could be obtained by scientists working only during the summers or by those working on random shipments of specimens, but only a researcher on the spot, or one able to make collections with invariable regularity and frequency, could come up with results of such quantitative significance.

Michael and G. F. McEwen, both of them young men who had in a sense grown up with the institution, worked jointly on a number of projects. In 1913 and 1914 they prepared a vast amount of field data, covering the entire period of the station's existence, for publication. Approximately 3000 temperatures and 2000 densities were recorded, as well as 3450 biological net hauls, 4336 water samples, and smaller numbers of various other observations. Beginning in 1915 the two men began working out statistical methods that could be applied to the data assembled in the researches on plankton and its environment. Their paper in this field was published in 1919, and greatly aided the work of the survey as a whole in that the method they had worked out on chaetognatha could be effectively applied to other species, saving other investigators much time and effort.

Michael also carried on distributional studies on the species *Salpa democratica*, helped develop more effective collecting apparatus, and was one of the first of the institution's staff to make full use of the pier in collecting plankton and investigating their distribution. Using the findings of McEwen and others on the phenomena of upwelling waters and ocean temperatures he began to relate these factors to the movements of plankton. Early in 1920 Michael was enabled to make a three months' collecting trip through the Bahamas and the Panama Canal on E. W. Scripps' yacht *Kemah*, but became ill a few months after his return and died on August 30, 1920, at the age of thirty-nine. He had been connected with the institution and its work for fifteen years. In the journal *Ecology* Ritter wrote, "The significance for ecology, and especially for marine ecology, of Michael's life work, though now recognized as considerable, will, it seems probable, be more clearly and fully seen later on."[4]

Another valuable body of work involving the relationship between ocean life and its environment was prosecuted over a period of more than twenty years by C. O. Esterly of Occidental College. Esterly worked only one full year at the institution but regularly spent his summers there and even dealt quantitatively with copepod collections, at one time as many as seventy per week, sent to him at Occidental. His studies of the minute crustacean copepoda involved the food and mode of feeding of these organisms as well as their movements and distribution. Esterly also published papers on the migration of the ctenophora, or "comb jellies," and the small phosphorescent crustacean order of schizopoda. During the year 1916-1917, which he spent at the institution, he carried on laboratory experiments on the causes of such movements among pelagic animals. Esterly received some compensation for this important part-time work, but the amount was never large.

C. A. Kofoid, after he succeeded Ritter as head of the University of California's Department of Zoology, did not spend long periods of time at La Jolla. He did maintain close contacts with the research station, however, and for a number of years after 1912 the institution employed someone to assist Kofoid with his studies of dinoflagellata and to keep him supplied with specimens. In 1920 he and Dr. Olive Swezy, who had helped him bring the work to completion, published *The Free-Living Unarmed Dinoflagellata*, a 538-page volume which was the culmination of at least twenty years of effort. Ritter, claiming a "large and vital" share for the institution in this publication, regarded it as "a focal point in the Institution's programme of investigation of 'ocean pasturage' of the north-eastern Pacific."[5]

Various graduate students and many of the summer researchers continued investigations on plankton, but of the permanent staff, no one else devoted himself solely to this field during the remaining years of Ritter's directorate. Two successive librarians carried on part-time zoological research. Dr. S. Stillman Berry, first hired as librarian in 1913, did "home work" on the chitons of the mollusk family, while Dr. Christine Essenberg spent her extra-library hours studying the transparent tadpole-like appendiculariae. Winfred E. Allen, who began working summers at the institution in 1917, carried on extensive investigations of the phytoplankton, especially the diatoms, that group of one-celled plants which are so important a part of the fundamental food supply of the ocean. In 1919 Allen was hired to continue these investigations and to serve as part-time "publicity secretary," charged with writing up the results of the institution's researches for the public press.

Studies of physical oceanography were prosecuted under the direction of G. F. McEwen, the young physicist from Stanford whom Ritter had begun to groom for the permanent staff in 1908. This area of the institution's program, it will be remembered, was originally held to be subordinate to the investigations on plankton, serving only to provide specific information on the environment of the organisms being studied. But very soon the institution's staff became aware that there were exciting discoveries to be made regarding the physics and chemistry of the ocean, and that various aspects of these fields were worthy of study apart from their relationship to the plankton and other forms of ocean life.

This does not mean that McEwen and his associates did not make valuable contributions to the survey as it was originally planned. In addition to helping E. L. Michael prepare the raw field data for publication and work out a statistical method for application to plankton, McEwen prepared hundreds of charts and graphs based on the thousands of observations made since the station's establishment. This concentrated and usable information on temperatures, salinity, currents, and other physical and chemical phenomena was extremely valuable to the other researchers attempting to reach conclusions about the relation of ocean life to its environment. In 1916, McEwen and Michael devised a combined plankton net, water bottle and thermometer which was a great improvement over the collecting apparatus which had been used formerly. This development eliminated the possibility that a costly error of two years before, when three weeks of work with the *Alexander Agassiz* had been virtually wasted, would be repeated. In 1914, after three weeks of intensive biological collecting, it had been discovered that the water bottle had not closed regularly at the intended depth, with the result that the biological samples were made "wholly worthless for the particular problem aimed at."[6] McEwen developed a way to measure the closing depth, and on the whole the new apparatus was much more sure and simpler to use.

The "oceanographic department"—those studying the physics and chemistry of the ocean—of course made many other direct contributions to Ritter's survey of the Pacific. One of McEwen's main areas of study, however, and one which probably brought more attention to the institution than any other line of investigation at this time, was the field of long-range weather forecasting. McEwen had been interested in the relationship between ocean temperatures and the climate of the adjacent coast since shortly after he had joined the institution's staff. By 1918 there seemed to be enough evidence to support the theory that negative temperature departures are followed by positive departures in seasonal rainfall, and visa-versa, to justify sending out a seasonal weather prediction to western businessmen having a particular interest in the amount and distribution of winter rains. The San Diego Chamber of Commerce cooperated in sending out letters, and the U. S. Weather Bureau helped assemble and analyze data. From 1912 on records were kept at a number of points along the north Pacific coast, with the cooperation of private and governmental agencies, and the institution kept an eye to the weather and weather forecasting until the mid-thirties, when the detailed work of assembling and analyzing these records was taken over by the U. S. Weather Bureau. This information on temperatures, salinity, and weather conditions so widely and regularly gathered also proved valuable in other aspects of the institution's program.

McEwen continued his studies of ocean temperatures as related to circulation, density, solar radiation and other physical factors, publishing several papers on these subjects. In 1919 he and N. W. Cummings, a graduate student and assistant for several years, began to study evaporation from fresh water reservoirs in the vicinity of San Diego in order to formulate mathematically certain problems of temperature and evaporation common to all bodies of water. At about the same time Eric G. Moberg, then a candidate for the doctor's degree, began important investigations on the chemistry of the sea. Despite the institution's skeletal year-round staff, knowledge of the physics and chemistry of the ocean advanced rapidly, and the growing importance of this aspect of the program was recognized by Ritter and other members of the staff and administration. An increasing amount of space in the annual reports of the director of the Scripps Institution for Biological Research to the President of the University of California was devoted to "physical oceanography" and, before long, "chemical oceanography," with planktology eventually relegated to a small section near the end of each report.

Such advances in the institution's program are not surprising in light of the evident dedication and industry of the permanent staff. They were willing to work long hours, even to suffer indignities, for the sake of science. This news item of 1922, concerning a collecting trip made by McEwen, Moberg and an assistant, will serve to illustrate:

[85]

Last Saturday night Dr. McEwen and Mr. Moberg and Mr. Woodward made a series of hourly collections of water samples at the Mission Bay Bridge. They remained through most of Sunday so as to get a variety of conditions of the tides. The intention was to see how the bay affected the temperature, saltiness and other conditions of the water which flows back and forth under the bridge. Late in the night someone who thought their equipment of bottles looked suspicious evidently informed the prohibition officer, as someone came and asked them a number of questions and looked at the contents of their bottles.[7]

There were other activities at the biological station which might have been regarded with suspicion by the uninformed. One of the most unusual research projects ever conducted there was being carried on during this period when the cluster of buildings was known as the Scripps Institution for Biological Research. This was Francis B. Sumner's study of heredity and environmental influence in the genus of mice *Peromyscus*.

The decision to devote a rather large percentage of the institution's budget, which previously had been used solely for research on marine organisms and their environment, to a study of land-dwelling mammals, was not made easily. "There is a strong feeling on the part of most if not all the Board members that it would not be wise to scatter our energies and resources," Ritter reported to Sumner when his application first came under consideration.[8] Sumner was at that time Naturalist with the U. S. Fisheries steamer *Albatross*, doing work in which he was experienced and competent, but which lay outside of his main scientific interest in genetics. As he had learned more of the Scripps Institution for Biological Research, through his official contacts with Kofoid and Ritter as *Albatross* Naturalist, he had become convinced that the institution might afford a unique opportunity for him to take up the investigations in which he was most interested. Thus on February 1, 1913, he set forth his proposed program of "experimental evolution" in a long letter to Ritter, stating that he felt "a very rich reward awaits the institution that blazes the trail" in this field.

The proposal came at an opportune time, as the state legislature's appropriation, part of which had been designated for an addition to the research staff, was soon assured. Also, less than a year before, when explaining the institution's change in name in his annual report, Ritter expressed the feeling of himself and the board that the institution "ought to have the utmost freedom as to the particular provinces of the vast domain of biology that it should cultivate at different periods of its existence."[9] Thus the stage was set for an addition to the institution of both a staff member and a new line of research.

Ritter was able to persuade the other members of the local board that Sumner and the problems he had posed were relevant to the rest of the institution's program. "The question of whether to take up the problem of acquired characters would be to 'scatter' our forces depends on what correlating principle determines our course," he wrote. "If materials to be worked on rather than problems to be worked at be the principle, then the expansion of activities from marine invertebrate plankton to terrestrial mammals would undoubtedly be a scattering. On the other hand, if the question of the relation of organisms to their environment be the coordinative principle, work on land animals and plants would not be at all a 'scatter.' "[10]

So late in 1913 F. B. Sumner joined the staff of the Scripps Institution for Biological Research, and began a series of experiments that were to cover a seventeen-year period. The various subspecies of Peromyscus, which he collected on field trips to different parts of California and even to other states, became the subjects of a wide range of experiments. For one of these Sumner brought mice from a variety of California climates—northern and southern, coastal and inland—and began to raise them in La Jolla's southern coastal climate, where a special mouse dormitory, or *murarium*, had been built to house them. The object of this experiment was to see if the different subspecies would show evidence of change in type in the direction of the local subspecies under the influence of the La Jolla climate. Eventually restricted to two widely-differing subspecies from the Mojave Desert and Humboldt County, this experiment was closed after eight years and six years, respectively, when the two races showed "not the least trace of convergence under the influence of a common environment."[11] Other experiments along the same line included subjecting several subspecies to an artificially dry climate and collecting and examining the differences, particularly in color and bodily proportions, among races of mice from greatly different climates and geological backgrounds.

Sumner also conducted many experiments in breeding with his races of Peromyscus, not only for quantitative studies in hybridization, but also on problems such as mutation and the inheritance of differences due to artifically induced differences in function. In his final report as Director of the Scripps Institution, written in 1923, Ritter had this to say of Sumner's work to that point:

It is fair to say, I think, that these investigations are unique in at least one respect: they embody a more serious effort to combine critical work in the taxonomy, distribution and genetics of the subspecies of a single full-fledged species than has hitherto been made. From the standpoint of the ideas that have determined the research policy of the Scripps Institution during the last decade and more, this is important as a concrete illustration of that idea.

Sumner's investigations were unique in another way in that the colony soon found itself responsible for the welfare of the hundreds of tiny denizens of the "mouse house." This was located in a canyon east of the other institution buildings to keep the mice safe from marauding cats, dogs and boys. The care and feeding of the mice, which at times numbered over a thousand, was a time-consuming and never-ending task. Usually Sumner was able to find an assistant for this work, although he supervised it and did most of the equally tedious labor of skinning, measuring and computing himself. When Sumner was absent from the station on field trips, lecturing at Berkeley or attending scientific meetings, however, Crandall, McEwen and even Ritter sometimes got in on the "mouse-sitting." In 1919 Sumner was away for several months giving a semester's work in Berkeley, and the institution hired a Mr. Warde to handle these duties full time. Sumner's careful instructions, in the form of a "Memorandum for Warde," included the following points:

Instruct Mrs. Warde in regular duties of feeding mice and guinea pigs so that she may do this if you should be sick.

Mice in open yard to be fed twice a week. Put in enough grain, sunflower seed and cactus for three or four days, but only enough mush for one day ... Give guinea pigs every day, rolled barley, fresh water, alfalfa hay, either cactus or green grass or other green food. One guinea pig eats as much as many mice.

Look out for dead or feeble mice whenever you feed.

Pregnant females or mothers of newly-born broods to be separated out as soon as discovered.

If a mouse escapes, catch immediately if possible, making sure to return it to same cage. If it is caught later and is a marked mouse put it back in cage to which you think it belongs. If not marked, put into a separate cage and make out a label stating what cage you think it came from.

Do not let anyone not a member of our staff (except Mrs. Warde) into the mouse house without a written permit either from Dr. Ritter or Mr. Crandall.[12]

Mr. Warde, doubtless tired of cutting up cactus and mixing mush, shortly moved on to a more lucrative position elsewhere, leaving the care of the mice in the hands of his seventeen-year-old brother-in-law, Wilford Granzow. This young man was to play a major role in the colony's first tragedy, which occurred on October 14, 1919, less than three weeks after he had assumed responsibility for Sumner's mice and guinea pigs.

Granzow and Mary B. Rudolph, a secretary and assistant who had been on the institution staff only about two months, went swimming in the early evening in the surf directly in front of the laboratory. Miss Rudolph, wading out too far, was caught by the undertow, and lost consciousness about the same time Granzow reached her and attempted to get her to shallow water. The two were carried under the pier where Granzow clung to a pile until members of the staff could lower life preservers and tow them ashore. Efforts to revive Miss Rudolph proved futile, and young Granzow was so weakened by the ordeal that he spent the next three days in bed. As Crandall also happened to be away, the unhappy tasks of informing Miss Rudolph's parents of her drowning and shipping the body to their home in Denver fell to Ritter, who also had to help out in the mouse house for a few days.

Ritter, from the time he moved to La Jolla in 1909, was never again able to devote even the major portion of his time to his own scientific research. He soon learned that directing the activities of a research institution, particularly a young and struggling one, required a variety of talents and immeasurable quantities of patience and adaptability. His interest in and knowledge of the work of each staff member was, as Sumner pointed out, practically the only unifying force in the institution's program and plans. Although W. C. Crandall relieved him of routine business matters and many administrative details, Ritter was left with numerous other duties. He frequently addressed civic groups, scientific conferences and educational meetings on the Scripps Institution and its work. Always there was writing to be done—countless letters and reports, articles for publication in *Science* and other scientific journals, and whatever book or article he was currently working on in connection with his own reading and research in biological philosophy. In 1918 alone, he sent three books—*The Higher Usefulness of Science and Other Essays*, the two-volume *The Unity of the Organism or the Organismal Conception of Life*, and *The Probable Infinity of Nature and Life*—to the publishers. The completion of these books at this particular time becomes more impressive when one realizes that they were finished during World War I.

The entry of the United States into the war brought many changes to the institution and new responsibilties to Ritter. As Director of Operations for the U. S. Bureau of Fisheries in southern California, and in connection with the institution's other activities during the war, Ritter was faced with the problem of obtaining maximum results with a staff which had been cut to the minimum.

The institution's specific war work was in two areas—kelp harvesting and fisheries. Crandall had undertaken a survey of the kelp beds off the Pacific coast for the U. S. Department of Agriculture as early as 1911, and had been concerned with such problems as the plant's rate of growth and its use as fertilizer since that time. For several years prior to the war he had been a special agent for the U. S. Bureau of Soils, charged with obtaining information on kelp and its uses and keeping the government informed of attempts to manufacture and market fertilizer from this source. Thus Crandall and the institution were the likely instruments in the government's wartime efforts to increase the production of fertilizer from kelp. One of Crandall's chief responsibilities was to advise the State Game and Fish Commission as to when various kelp beds should be declared "open" and when "closed" in regard to harvesting. In addition to general inquiry carried on concerning the extent and rate of growth of the kelp beds, special botanical investigations were conducted on such problems as the plant's mode of propagation and susceptibility to bacterial infection.

In connection with the fisheries industry the Scripps Institution cooperated with several government agencies. Under the auspices of the U. S. Bureau of Fisheries investigations on the distribution and "life habits" of the long-finned albacore, or tuna, were carried out—

hopefully to obtain information which would increase the catch. The laboratory facilities were also used for experiments on methods of preserving fish, other than canning, in cooperation with the U. S. Bureau of Chemistry and the Federal Food Administration. A third and more long-range program, partially financed by the Council of Defense of California, aimed at "bringing the institution's program of research on the 'plankton' as the fundamental food supply of commercial fishes, and in the hydrography of the fishing area, as part of the environment of the fishes, into the service of the fishing industry."[13] Finally, the institution yielded the services of W. C. Crandall, who, as Fish Administrator for southern California with the National Food Administration, had little time left over to devote to the station's business affairs.

Crandall's regular duties were somewhat lessened in this period, however, by the fact that the *Alexander Agassiz* had been sold in January, 1917. The reason given for the sale in Ritter's report to the president of the university was that the boat was "too large and expensive to operate for the particular phase of the marine investigations we are now entering upon." After a "checkered career" in the Mexican coast trade, during which she was once seized on suspicion of being a German privateer,[14] the *Agassiz* ended her days on the rocks near the entrance to San Francisco Bay late in 1920. The Scripps Institution conducted its wartime marine investigations primarily with rented boats and through arrangements with government agencies and private commercial interests.

The First World War was the first period when the Scripps Institution carried on large scale projects in cooperation with the state and federal governments, initiating a practice that was to become increasingly important in later years. In the eyes of some members of the local community, the scientists at the "bug house" carried their cooperation too far. At the height of the spy scare Ritter's secretary-assistant, who was later drafted, came under suspicion because he spoke German. Not long afterwards some over-zealous La Jolla patriots, who from the hills above town had watched the swinging lantern of the night-watchman as he made his nightly trek to the end of the pier and back, accused the institution of signalling German ships at sea.[15] Some, at least, of Sumner's "community of laymen" were doing their part to prolong the institution's isolation.

CHAPTER IX

A NEW KIND OF INSTITUTION

THE FIRST WORLD WAR, as evidenced by the wartime activities of the Scripps Institution, clearly demonstrated the need for greater knowledge of the Pacific Ocean and wiser utilization of its resources. As Ritter expressed it, the United States, bordered as it was by two great oceans, could no longer afford to regard these vast bodies of water merely as "a world highway and fighting arena." Soon all nations must recognize the importance of the sea as a producer of food and other necessities, as a basal factor in the physical environment of their peoples, and as "a great field in which man's irresistible spirit of adventure and discovery finds room to exercise itself."[1] With the growth of world population maritime industries would become far more important from an economic standpoint, and the need for some kind of regulation to insure against depletion of the sea's resources was bound to increase.

The Scripps Institution found itself in a unique position in regard to the emerging problems of the world's oceans. The government's wartime search for experienced men to direct its special programs of marine research in the Pacific had soon led it to the University of California's biological research station. Although they had necessarily concentrated their efforts in a relatively small area, Director Ritter and the staff members of the Scripps Institution had at least made a beginning on an organized program of oceanic investigation. Their knowledge of biological and physical aspects of the sea, and of specific methods of increasing that knowledge, qualified them for leadership positions in a field where qualified men were far too few. Thus the government's plans for exploration of the Pacific relied heavily from the beginning on the staff and experience of the Scripps Institution.

In 1919 a Pacific Exploration Committee was set up by the

National Research Council of the American Academy of Sciences and both Ritter and McEwen were appointed members. Within two years this body was consolidated and placed under the Division of Foreign Relations of the NRC, for reasons which Ritter had once outlined as follows:

The sea and the atmosphere are preeminent among the features of the earth as the common physical heritage and bond among peoples and nations. So it happens that the scientific questions presented by these two realms are in their very essence common to many peoples. They are fundamentally interstate and international. Nowhere does the great idea of internationalism now so much in the world's mind find a broader, more definite, more secure footing than in these realms and the scientific treatment of them.[2]

The purpose of the reorganized Committee of Pacific Investigation was to set forth the problems then being explored, formulate others in immediate need of investigation, and point out what would be necessary to carry out such researches, as well as what agencies, whether private or governmental, could best prosecute them.

The Pacific Division of the American Association for the Advancement of Science organized a Committee on Conservation of Marine Life of the Pacific in 1921. W. C. Crandall was appointed one of five members of this committee, which, though it cooperated with the larger division of the National Research Council, aimed at defining and solving much more specific problems. Both Crandall and P. S. Barnhart were able to make valuable contributions to plans for studying the life habits of the important commercial fishes of the Pacific and for conserving marine resources such as the rapidly diminishing fur seal herds.

If national committees had to depend on the training and experience of men such as those at the Scripps Institution, the scientists, in turn, looked to departments of the government as the only agencies capable of initiating and maintaining such extensive and long-continued investigations as would be necessary. To begin with, part of the field work could be done by the regular ships and officers of the U. S. Navy or those of the U. S. Coast and Geodetic Survey with little interference with their regular routines. Observations at various points along the coast might be made by men stationed at U. S. lighthouses or by cooperating marine institutions such as Stanford's Hopkins Laboratory at Pacific Grove. Indeed, some of these cooperative ventures were begun during and immediately after the First World War, but not without a great deal of time and effort spent in the work of liaison and organization.

Such duties naturally fell chiefly to Ritter, who in the years between the war and his retirement in 1923 spent a large portion of his time away from La Jolla. As a member of the major American scientific societies, Ritter represented the institution at numerous conferences and constantly worked among his associates to generate interest in and support for his program of organized biological research. Having to give speeches or even sit through long meetings was not always to his liking. During a lengthy sojourn in Washington, D. C., in 1921, he wrote to Crandall at La Jolla:

The number of things I am into here—and am in danger of getting into is somewhat alarming to one like myself, whose tastes are not exactly for boisterous science.[3]

Not all of Ritter's short trips and more prolonged absences were directly related to the affairs of the Scripps Institution for Biological Research, however. He was also becoming very much involved in another "Scripps enterprise," and to fulfill his duties as President of "Science Service," took a six-months leave of absence from the institution in 1921. Originally formed as "Science News Service" in 1919, the organization was one product of years of conversation and speculation between Ritter and E. W. Scripps. Both had long felt that one of the "duties" of the Scripps Institution for Biological Research, and of all such institutions, was to make the results of its researches available in a popular form to the public. Various experiments along these lines had been tried by Ritter and his staff almost from the station's beginning. Based on the premises that (1) an intelligent and well-informed *demos* was absolutely essential to a democracy, (2) the dominating and thus most important ideas of the modern era were those of science; and (3) the most widespread and continuous means of disseminating *any* information was the public press, Science Service began operations in 1921.

The initial organization included three representatives from each of the following groups: The National Academy of Sciences, the American Association for the Advancement of Science, the National Research Council and the journalistic profession. In addition E. W. Scripps, his son Robert, and Ritter were listed as members representing the "E. W. Scripps Estate." Although it was hoped that Science Service would soon become self-supporting—paying scientists for their contributions and selling the articles to newspapers—E. W. Scripps provided a large amount of "working capital" to set the project on its feet. Ritter was the corporation's first president, and did much of the organizational work, although his most active period in connection with Science Service was postponed until after his retirement from the directorship of the Scripps Institution.

During Ritter's absences in the early twenties the program of the institution went on with relative smoothness and continuity. Much of the work—collecting and quantitative analysis of plankton, the gathering of hydrographical data, Sumner's measurements and calculations—had become established routine. The physical plant, although it was somewhat crowded in the busy summer months, was still adequate for the needs of the regular staff. The cottages especially were much in demand during the vacation periods; even the Ritters' house was rented during their six-months stay in Washington in 1921. The occupant, Dr. Walter P. Taylor, kept the Ritters well-informed of exciting colony events:

There is little in the way of news, except that Dr. Norris is back again, and that various linnets are nesting about your house, and the same rabbit is living under your saltbush. A black phoebe is nesting on the back of your garage . . .[4]

The largest share of the responsibility of running the station was taken by W. C. Crandall, who efficiently handled business matters, tried to keep the buildings and grounds in repair, and at times must have felt like the manager of a summer vacation resort. A great variety of visitors, only some of them scientists and their families, occupied the institution's two dozen cottages for periods ranging from a few days to as long as six months or more. With preliminary arrangements to take care of, trains to meet, luggage to pick up, introductions to make and innumerable other such tasks involved with each guest, Crandall undoubtedly kept busy. He still found time, however, to report various happenings to Ritter, and even went into detail on staff meetings:

A second matter was the appropriateness of having in the outside reading room a Socialist paper, "The World," and it was decided that it was best not to flaunt such a paper in our public reading room as this particular paper is like waving a red flag in this particular locality.[5]

Some decisions the staff could make, but they never failed to consult Ritter on matters of policy and long-range needs and financing. On questions affecting the institution's future Ritter remained the chief oracle.

There was some disagreement over what the future should be. Crandall, who beginning in 1921 made a series of yearly reports on the institution's affairs to Miss Scripps, each time expressed his strong opinion that the institution should concentrate on marine biology, as it was "impossible to distribute a limited fund over a number of activities and achieve greatly in any one." He also stated that he looked forward to the time when the institution could devote itself to "what was originally the main work."[6]

This feeling may have been shared by some of the staff members working on the marine biological phase of the program, but these were by now in the minority. In his 1923 report to Miss Scripps, Crandall broke down the salary schedule as follows, including secretaries and assistants as well as faculty:[7]

General Administration $10,910
Marine Biology 8,750
Philosophical Biology 3,660
Hydrography 6,300
Genetics and Heredity 5,240

The "philosophical biology" portion of Crandall's chart would be changed to something else in 1923, but until shortly before Ritter's retirement no one was certain who the new director would be and what might be his particular interest. Ritter's first choice, a Harvard zoologist who would have welcomed the chance to carry on his own research at La Jolla, was forced to decline for family reasons. The problem became such a difficult one that although Ritter reached retirement age in 1922, he was persuaded to extend his directorship for an additional year. Much of that year he devoted to looking for a successor and making plans for the institution's future, spending many long hours in discussion with some of the leading scientific men of the country, officials of the university, and representatives of state and national government agencies. On November 15, 1922, Ritter summed up the results of these conferences in a letter inviting Sir W. A. Herdman, one of the world's leading oceanographers, to come to the United States to give a series of lectures on oceanic research:

The time has now come for me to retire from the directorship of the Scripps Institution and everybody concerned is joining with me in a somewhat anxious effort to get me out and the right man in. The great thing at issue is this: A rather wide circle of scientific men in America are now convinced that the Institution we have developed on the coast of Southern California ought to be treated as a nucleus for an oceanographic institution worthy of the magnitude of the oceanographic problems of the largest ocean now on earth and one of the richest countries on earth.[8]

Also in November, the name of T. Wayland Vaughan was first mentioned in connection with these conferences on the institution's future. "Vaughan was drawn in because of his previous interest and wide knowledge of Pacific Investigation matters," Ritter wrote. "He is the virtual chairman of the Committee on Pacific Investigation of the National Research Committee." Ritter went on to comment on "the outstanding position of Vaughan in relation to the whole matter."[9]

In March of 1923 the whole matter was still uncertain—at least as far as the institution staff were concerned. "We are about through with our present director and it is not known who his successor is to be," Crandall wrote one of his associates. "It may be a man by the name of Vaughan from Washington. A geologist with a hankering for coral reefs."[10]

T. Wayland Vaughan, at that time with the U. S. Geological Survey, did indeed seem to be the best man to direct the work of the country's first oceanographic institution, and he was included in further conferences. Dr. Vaughan's geological interest in the sedimentary deposits of the ocean floor had led him to a study of the corals and foraminifera and their role in the formation of land masses, and he had become the leading American authority on these groups—"a biologist in spite of himself," as Sumner put it.[11] His work in Washington had put him in close touch with the federal scientific agencies whose cooperation would be absolutely necessary in carrying out a large-scale program of oceanic research. Thus President-elect Campbell wired Vaughan asking him to accept the directorship in April, 1923.

Vaughan replied in the affirmative, subject to the conditions that (1) he be permitted to finish up his own oceanographic investigations; (2) he be granted a travel allowance sufficient to allow him to maintain contacts with other scientists and institutions; (3) the institution's program be extended as soon as posssible to marine sediments and the chemistry and bacteriology of the sea; and (4) a few minor requests be granted. The president and regents readily agreed to these conditions.

Vaughan's final acceptance was wired to Ritter and the university officials on May 1, 1923, less than two months before Ritter was scheduled to leave the institution for Australia and the Pacific Science Congress to be held there in July and August. Vaughan visited the institution for a few days in early June, meeting the staff and looking over the buildings and equipment for the first time. Then he and Ritter went to Berkeley for final conferences with W. W. Campbell, by now installed as president of the university.

Ritter returned from Berkeley to spend his last two weeks as director of the institution he had created—weeks of finishing touches and farewells. The Ritters had made La Jolla their home for more than fifteen years, and it was not easy to tear up their roots and start a new life. Mrs. Ritter left a week ahead of her husband, who tersely recorded the final few days in his diary:

June 23rd. Drove from Miss Scripps to the Institution. Ate my cold lunch in yard of our home, alone, with many stirring thoughts. Our empty home ... very empty ... *Tuesday, June 24th*. Beautiful day ... Last conferences with staff, devoted to last touches of getting ready to leave tomorrow . . . Luncheon at Spindrift, guest of the Crandalls . . . Feelings such as never experienced before at last leave-taking of house at 5:30 ... Last dinner with the Harpers. *June 25th*. Last breakfast with Miss Scripps ... off for San Diego via Dr. Baker's for farewells to Dr. Charlotte and Dr. Fred . . . latter to train with me . . .[12]

As T. Wayland Vaughan was also a delegate to the Pacific Science Congress, and as he, like Ritter, had planned to visit other parts of the South Pacific after the meetings in Australia, there would be a six-months lapse between directors at the Scripps Institution. F. B. Sumner agreed to serve as Acting Director during the interim.

Obviously Sumner was the staff member most directly affected by the change in policy of the Scripps Institution. Although Ritter had tried to insure the continuation of Sumner's investigations on Peromyscus, Sumner later noted in his autobiography that he himself "foresaw as much as anyone what an incongruous situation it would be for a considerable proportion of the income of an oceanographic institution to be devoted to the study of mice."[13]

At one point during his brief tenure as Acting Director Sumner made a general speech on the Scripps Institution, describing its facilities, its program, and its staff members. He finished up with a brief statement of what he understood was to be the future program and policy of the institution, expressing his regret that the new director could not be present to make this more clear, and concluded:

There is doubtless need enough for an oceanographic institution, of perhaps international scope, and it may well be that the Scripps Institution has been wisely chosen as the nucleus of such an organization. But it may be permissable to say, in conclusion, that if such a course is adopted there will be left a great gap to be filled. We shall then need a new institution which shall be in the words of our Regents, "an instrument for the most liberal biological research," one in which the problems of biology are kept in the foreground, and where the material for study may be chosen without reference to whether it chances to be marine or terrestrial in its habitat.[14]

So although in one sense the Scripps Institution's new policy was a broadening of its existing activities, it was in another sense a narrowing and curtailing of other activities, and there were bound to be valid objections. The institution had reflected the ideas of its chief sponsors and its director, and ideas are subject to revision. Ritter, Presidents Barrows and Campbell of the university, E. W. Scripps and the others they had consulted were well aware that in selecting the new director of the Scripps Institution they were determining the shape the institution would take in the future. At the very least, the choice of Vaughan guaranteed that from that time on investigations of the physical aspects of the Pacific would be on an equal footing with the biological investigations.

Vaughan began his term of office on February 1, 1924, and even in his first few months brought about some changes. One of these was the abolition of the office of business manager, and Vaughan's assumption of the management of both the business and the scientific work of the institution. In his first report to the president of the university, dated July 1, 1924, Vaughan stated that "W. C. Crandall, former business manager, resigned at the end of April, after a long term of faithful service. He preferred resigning to being transferred to other work under the office of the Comptroller of the University."

Crandall became a business agent for Ellen Scripps and thus continued to be involved to some degree in the institution's affairs. In the same report Vaughan announced his intention of transferring Sumner and his "important researches" to Berkeley, but this was never feasible. Reluctant as he was to abandon these studies, which had begun to yield significant results, during the next few years Sumner gradually brought various phases of them to a close, and turned to largely physiological investigations on fishes.

Vaughan soon arranged for the collection and study of marine sediments, which, according to a feature writer for the San Diego *Sun*, he referred to as "my beloved bottom muds."[15] Investigations of the chemistry of the sea, primarily in biochemistry, had been seriously begun by E. G. Moberg while he was a graduate assistant during Ritter's last years, and Moberg became a permanent staff member with the advent of Vaughan's administration. Thus the institution's work could now be divided into four areas—physical, chemical, biological and geological oceanography—with Sumner's studies gradually being brought into conformity. Vaughan's first few annual reports emphasize the urgent need for added assistance in some of these areas, as the institution's funds were understandably not allocated evenly among them.

During Vaughan's era the financial picture did begin to brighten, largely due to the sincere interest and active support of President W. W. Campbell, who had been director of the Lick Observatory and was perhaps more sensitive to the importance and real needs of a semi-independent research institution than other presidents could have been. When Vaughan became director, in 1924, the state appropriation to the institution was $22,500 per year, and had been for several years. This sum was approximately matched by Miss Scripps' regular donation of $9000, special yearly donations from E. W. Scripps of about $5000, and receipts from rentals and the supply department of the institution of about $7500. In November of 1924 President Campbell proposed that the state and the Scrippses continue this "matching" policy in increasing the income of the institution $5000 per year (each party adding $2500) during the following four years. This meant that in the fourth year the state and private donors would each be giving $10,000 more than they were contributing in 1924-25.

President Campbell's four-year plan would not have been too great a strain on Miss Scripps' finances had it not been that 1924-25 was the last year that E. W. Scripps made his $5000 contribution. So that the work of the institution would not be seriously hampered, Miss Scripps agreed to take over her brother's contribution as well as her own. Thus in 1925-26 she gave $7500 more than her usual $9000, but could make commitments only a year at a time. In Vaughan's second full year as director, then, the institution's income was almost $50,000 per year, and hopefully would increase rapidly enough to allow for the needed expansion in several areas of oceanic research.

Miss Scripps, by this time well into her eighties, could no longer take an active role in making policy decisions for the institution. The local board of directors, which originally had been set up to retain a degree of local control during her lifetime, had ceased to function by the time Vaughan became director, although he attempted to include its remaining members in an advisory board which he later set up. As is evident from the communications between Ritter and the staff on the matter of a new director, policy decisions were largely removed from the local scene after the First World War. It is also evident from these communications, however, that E. W. Scripps was still a major influence in the institution's affairs, as he had been since the formation of the original Marine Biological Association in 1903.

E. W. never established an income-producing endowment, as Ellen Scripps did, but he had largely influenced his sister's contributions and had, as has been indicated, awakened her initial interest. In addition, E. W. made yearly donations to the institution for more than twenty years, in variable amounts which depended mostly on his conversations with Ritter about the institution's specific needs. In 1919-20 for example, E. W. provided $4200 for the salaries of assistants in genetics, oceanography and stenographic work; $2500 for Michael and Crandall's collecting trip on his yacht *Kemah*; $1800 for library purchases; $1150 for Sumner's field trips; and $2000 in publication funds. Ordinarily his contributions for specific purposes were nearer $5000 per year, but provided a degree of valuable flexibility in financing a program where unforeseen needs could so easily arise. E. W.'s giving was never an automatic gesture; he seemed to need to be convinced of the worth of whatever activities he supported.

Some of the ideas which E. W. had hoped to see embodied in the

Scripps Institution, ideas which he was willing to underwrite financially, eventually found expression elsewhere. He had once considered establishing a study of anthropoid apes at the La Jolla institution, and at another time wanted to introduce a department of sociology. E. W.'s primary interest was people, and science in so far as it could benefit man. With Ritter's help he started the Scripps Foundation for Problems of Population at Miami University in Oxford, Ohio, and in Science Service set up a means of disseminating the scientific knowledge he considered so valuable.

During the war E. W. suffered a stroke and was afterwards forced to greatly curtail his activities. Retiring in 1920 from all newspaper responsibilities, he began to spend more and more time on his yacht. Even as a virtual "floating recluse" he still gave some attention to the affairs of the Scripps Institution. He and Ritter exchanged lengthy letters on a variety of subjects, and managed to get together, as they had done so often in the institution's early years, for long hours of conversation. In the winter of 1922-23, Ritter accompanied E. W. on a leisurely trip through the Caribbean, along the northern coast of South America, through the Panama Canal and up the coast of Mexico, and a great many plans for the Scripps Institution and Science Service were laid. "Very important talks with E. W. on heredity, Institution affairs, and consciousness," Ritter noted in his diary on January 30, 1923.[16]

On March 12, 1926, E. W. Scripps died of apoplexy on his yacht *Ohio* off the coast of Monrovia, Liberia. He had already transferred control of his business interests to his son Bob, and had insured that all of the various enterprises he had begun would go smoothly on without him. Although his will included no financial provision for the Institution, his legacy was a real one. Most of those most closely associated with the institution felt that it would never have been more than a summer marine laboratory had it not been for E. W. Scripps and his relationship with Ritter. Perhaps C. A. Kofoid best described this relationship in an unpublished manuscript prepared for Ritter's seventieth birthday a few years later:

There grew up from the very first a close and ever enlarging intellectual attachment and personal friendship between Dr. Ritter and Mr. Scripps. The attachment between the men rested upon a mutual understanding of certain rather deep-seated motives which guided these two men, who otherwise differed greatly in almost all particulars. The one was a masterful, dominating man of affairs, with a largely assumed indifference to culture and refinement, but withal with the keenest of intellectual grasp of the world's thought and life, and, under the mask of realism, a great idealist. The other came from the academic shades with the aspirations of the idealist and a program devoid of all immediate practical application. The two had this in common: both were inquirers, both were earnestly seeking the truth, and both were believers that the truth, science, would set men free, if only men could come to know the truth.

CHAPTER X

OCEANOGRAPHERS AGROUND

WHEN T. WAYLAND VAUGHAN agreed to become the new director of the Scripps Institution he did not inherit an easy task. Given a biological research station which had been somewhat arbitrarily assembled according to the needs and desires of its founders and full-time staff members, he was asked to create the hemisphere's first oceanographic institution. Such an assignment would have been difficult under the best of circumstances, and certainly with the limitations of facilities and financial resources to be found at La Jolla, it must have at the outset sometimes seemed an impossibility. When Vaughan assumed the directorship, on February 1, 1924, the institution thereafter to be dedicated to "the oceanographic problems of the largest ocean now on earth," did not even own a boat.

Vaughan was familiar enough with the science of oceanography in its international manifestations, however, to know what ingredients were missing from his potpourri for the study of the sea, and he painstakingly began to assemble them. The institution's name was officially changed to the Scripps Institution of Oceanography on October 14, 1925, but this move did not equip it for a full program of oceanic research. When Vaughan left the institution more than twelve years later the job was yet unfinished; despite new buildings and new men there was still an atmosphere of "making do" with some of the hand-me-downs of an earlier era.

In 1924 the institution consisted of the old G. H. Scripps laboratory, the museum-library, the somewhat dilapidated wooden aquarium building, two dozen cottages, a few small service and storage buildings, the director's residence and the pier, which was also badly in need of repair. The annual budget, which by that time was approaching $50,000 per year, had been consistently used mainly for salaries and the research work itself, with the result that the physical facilities had been allowed to sink gradually into what Vaughan called a "lamentable condition."[1] The new director, who evidently prized well-cared-for surroundings, was particularly chagrined by the condition of the institution's grounds, and immediately began to plant trees and shrubs around his own house and elsewhere on the grounds at his own expense—trees and shrubs that could survive the "windswept seaside environment." Guy L. Fleming, custodian of the Torrey Pines Reserve who resided at the institution, directed this early planting.[2]

Within a year or two Vaughan had commissioned a plan to be drawn up by a professor of landscape architecture from the university,[3] and over a period of several years thousands of trees and shrubs were planted according to this plan. By 1931 Vaughan could report that the planting program was "virtually completed." Having provided $650 a year for this purpose from his own funds, Vaughan had little trouble persuading the university and Miss Scripps to match his contribution. Donations of plants and seeds came from several sources, including the Australian Botanical Gardens, and many varieties were planted on an experimental basis to see if they would adapt to the Southern California climate. Large numbers of eucalyptus trees were added to those remaining from the earlier plantings of 1909-1910, and an acacia grove representing many varieties was planted on the plateau overlooking the institution's buildings. By the end of Vaughan's term the slopes of the institution's land looked decidedly less barren, due to his efforts to plant trees along the roadways and against the skyline.[4]

Staff members during Vaughan's era recall that one of the most vociferous of his rare displays of temper occurred in connection with the institution grounds and his planting program. A number of trees had been planted along a narrow roadway on the institution property, and it soon became obvious that the trees were already something of a hazard and would eventually block the road entirely. Consequently, at a meeting where the subject was discussed, the staff voted unanimously for the removal of the trees. Vaughan exploded. He had expended so much time, effort and money on the improvement of the grounds that the removal of any of his carefully-nurtured plants must have seemed a sacrilege. Faced with this virtual mutiny on the part of his ungrateful staff he heatedly threatened to pull out every tree on the property. Fortunately Vaughan never carried out his threat, and indeed left a legacy of planting that was much appreciated by subsequent residents of the Scripps Institution.

There are many colorful tales to be told of "the great Texas autocrat," who had left the cultural refinement and intellectual stimulation of Washington, D. C., to assume the management of the struggling little research institution on the edge of the Pacific.[5] Always attired in coat and tie, no matter what the weather, Vaughan on weekends would don a visor cap and with his German Shepherd dog make an inspection tour of the institution grounds. Early residents can remember his poking about in their gardens with his cane or cautioning them about wasting water in caring for their yards. Nevertheless, most of the staff respected Vaughan and what he was trying to do for the Scripps Institution. With the handicap of inadequate funds even landscaping the grounds was a constant struggle, and the problems of putting together an oceanographic institution were proportionately greater.

The "step-up" program for increasing the regular income of the institution, which President Campbell had proposed in 1925, was continued even into the thirties, despite the effects of the Depression on the state as well as the private sources. Although the income was thereby approximately doubled during Vaughan's administration, it increased so gradually that Vaughan had to be content with taking one step at a time toward the goals he had set for the institution. Primarily the increases were used for the salaries of scientists in new lines of research, and for assistants, with any surplus being carefully apportioned for the most vitally-needed equipment. Thus the imbalance among the disciplines Vaughan considered essential to a comprehensive oceanographic program was gradually corrected as funds became available.

An unexpected boon to the institution's work in physical oceanography, which was largely a result of G. F. McEwen's earlier attempts at long-range weather forecasting, came in 1925 and lasted into the Depression. In 1925 three Southern California light and power companies contributed a fund of $500 for the purchase of two thermographs for the measuring of ocean temperatures. On November 6 and 7 of that same year a conference on the physical oceanography and marine meteorology of the northeast Pacific and the climate of the western United States was held at the institution and drew in other interested parties. The conference led to increased participation in the collection of oceanographic data on the part of the U. S. Navy, the U. S. Bureau of Lighthouses, and the Los Angeles Steamship Company. By 1928 a dozen regional power companies had become interested enough in the meteorological research to contribute a fund of $6000, which was sufficient for the salaries of one full-time and two part-time investigators in this field. The fund had grown to $12,000 by 1932, which, due to the Depression, was the last year the companies were able to give this extra support.

With the combination of outside income and Vaughan's initial emphasis on building up research on the physical aspects of the ocean, the biological phase of the institution's program in the late twenties was temporarily neglected. C. O. Esterly, who had carried on part-time work on the zoo-plankton since the institution's beginning, died in 1928, leaving this important field, once the main part of the research program, entirely without a permanent investigator. Vaughan's first addition to the biological staff was in the field of marine bacteriology. A. Haldane Gee became the institution's first microbiologist on July 1, 1928. Gee left after a little more than two years, and the search for someone to replace him eventually led to the university's own department of bacteriology and Claude E. Zo-Bell who became microbiologist on January 1, 1932.

The next area of study to open up was that of the physiology of marine organisms. Investigations in this field had been carried on intermittently by various part-time workers through the years, but Denis L. Fox, who left Stanford to begin work September 1, 1931, was the first full-time physiologist on the institution staff.

Vaughan devoted a great deal of time and thought to each of his additions to the permanent staff. Scientific competence was, of course, of primary importance, but other factors had to be considered. Vaughan wrote one colleague:

Will you please let me know what you think of Mr. C— as a scientific possibility, with emphasis on his capacity for research, giving me as full information as you can regarding his personality. Is he bumptuous? Is he considerate of others? What kind of appearance does he present?[6]

Some of these considerations may have been more important to Vaughan than to some of the other staff members. The small size of the staff, however, and the fact that most of the scientists lived as well as worked on the institution grounds, made questions of personality much more significant.

Naturally the increases in personnel necessitated an increase in facilities, and the construction of a new laboratory was one of the major achievements of Vaughan's administration. The need for more working space had been felt for several years. By the late twenties the institution's own staff had grown so large that it was necessary to refuse space to visiting investigators. In 1929 the state legislature appropriated $40,000 toward a fund for the construction of a new laboratory building, and this sum was matched by Ellen Scripps. Miss Scripps preferred to remain "an anonymous donor" in this instance, and was so listed in newspaper accounts and even in Vaughan's report to the president of the university. Miss Scripps had always avoided publicity in making her contributions, and her desire for anonymity was more fully explained by Attorney J. C. Harper in 1919:

I am writing to urge that hereafter no publication be made using Miss Scripps' name in connection with any gift she may make to the University . . . An announcement that she has made a gift always brings upon her a raft of applications for assistance. These have always been annoying and in her present enfeebled health are a real burden that I know you will want to join the rest of us in relieving her from.[7]

With $80,000 thus provided by the state and Miss Scripps, plans went ahead to construct a new laboratory to be used primarily for work in physical and chemical oceanography and "those kinds of biological investigation which require either biochemical or biophysical methods."[8] The specialized laboratories and equipment would be expensive, and Vaughan and the committee responsible for planning the building were prepared to cut costs and do without important items to stay within the $80,000 limit. Thus it was an unexpected blessing to most of those involved when an additional $40,000 came through in April of 1930 from the Rockefeller Foundation, enabling the Scripps Institution to build "the best in modern laboratory facilities" for the type of work they were planning.

The grant was not a complete surprise to Vaughan, who had been among the scientists advising the Rockefeller Foundation on the expenditure of much larger sums for oceanographic research. In 1927, Vaughan had been appointed to the Committee on Oceanography of the National Academy of Sciences, formed "to consider the share of the United States of America in a world-wide program of oceanic research and report to the Academy."[9] As he was the director of what was then the only institution in the United States devoted to such research, he was destined to play a major role in making plans for the future of oceanography in this country.

The need for the evaluation and further development of oceanographic research in the United States was made clear in a statement which Frank R. Lillie, chairman of the committee, sent to the other members selected from the Academy.[10] "The interests of oceanography have not advanced as they should in the United States of America in comparison with several other countries," he wrote, "even though more money is spent on various isolated projects within the field."[11] The five committee members were quick to respond with specific proposals for consideration. Organized studies of the configuration of the ocean bottoms, measurements of the velocities and direction of ocean currents, and formation of an institution to specifically study the Atlantic, perhaps through the expansion of the Bermuda Biological Station, were listed among the most pressing needs in the area of oceanic investigation.

The National Academy obtained $75,000 for the work of the Committee on Oceanography from the Rockefeller-backed General Education Board, and a number of studies were carried out. Dr. Henry B. Bigelow of the Museum of Comparative Zoology at Harvard University was asked to compile a preliminary report for presentation to the Academy, and this was submitted in November, 1929.[12] In the thirties studies on the "international aspects of oceanography" and "oceanography in universities" were similarly commissioned. The Bigelow report, however, and the conference which the Committee on Oceanography held with representatives of the General Education Board and the Rockefeller Foundation in the late twenties, were largely responsible for what many regard as the greatest forward step in oceanographic research taken in the United States up to the Second World War. The major recommendation to grow out of the committee's investigations, and its major accomplishment, was the establishment of a "central oceanographic institution" on the Atlantic coast.[13]

The endowment of such an institution had been a part of the plans as early as 1925, when Wickliffe Rose, soon to retire as head of the

General Education Board, had first discussed the needs in oceanic research with Lillie, then director of the Marine Biological Laboratory at Woods Hole, Massachusetts. The formation of a committee by the National Academy of Sciences and that committee's official endorsement of the project gave a stamp of approval which prompted Dr. Max Mason and the Rockefeller Foundation, who took up the proposal on Rose's retirement, to provide $3 million for the establishment of an oceanographic institution at Woods Hole in 1930. Vaughan functioned as chief consultant in planning the Woods Hole facilities, allocation of finances and program, and was appointed to the original board of trustees. It must have been painful for him to see the ideals toward which he had so painstakingly worked for the Scripps Institution realized so immediately for the "sister institution" on the Atlantic. Woods Hole began life with fully-equipped laboratories and a 142-foot vessel, the *Atlantis*, designed specifically for oceanographic research. In 1935 the $1,000,000 income-producing endowment (which had been supplemented by $50,000 yearly during the first few years) was increased to $2,000,000, and an ample annual income was thus assured.

The Rockefeller Foundation also provided $50,000 for the "expansion and stabilization" of the Bermuda Biological Station for Research, which would complement the Woods Hole institution as a "truly oceanic" location. On the Pacific coast the major Rockefeller grant, $265,000, went to the University of Washington for the establishment of its Puget Sound oceanographic laboratories. The $40,000 contributed for the completion of the new laboratory building at the Scripps Institution was one of the smallest of the foundation's oceanographic favors.

It had been the feeling of several of the members of the Committee on Oceanography, from the beginning, that there was adequate provision for the study of oceanography on the Pacific coast due to the Scripps Institution and the "active policies" of its director. The glaring lack on the Atlantic coast of any institution whatsoever "committed to comprehensive oceanographic investigation," drew most of the attention to the east and held it there. In numerous letters and conferences Vaughan did what he could to counteract this trend. "I certainly hope that the Pacific side of the country is not going to be left out of the running," he wrote to Lillie in November of 1929. "As you know I wish the Institution with which I am connected strengthened and I think that additional consideration should be given both to the Pacific Grove group and those at the University of Washington."[14] Doubtless the comparatively small amounts which were put into oceanography on the Pacific coast were due largely to Vaughan's efforts, but he may have had reason to regret the fact that he and the Scripps Institution had gotten off to such an apparently-good "head start" in the field.

Nevertheless, the $40,000 Rockefeller grant brought to $120,000 the funds available for the new laboratory and proved a considerable boon to the Scripps Institution. The building, which the university regents named Ritter Hall, was ready for occupancy by September, 1931. Designed by Louis J. Gill, nephew of the architect of the first laboratory building, Ritter Hall was 100 feet long, 46 feet wide, and three stories high. On the top floor were the offices and laboratories of those working in physical and chemical oceanography and marine meteorology; on the middle level "suites" for bacteriology and physiology; and on the ground floor facilities for photographic work, a machinery room and transformer vault, two rooms intended for the large scale cultures of marine organisms, storage and future laboratory space.

The allocation of the new facilities had not been accomplished without some friction among the staff. One long-time staff member went so far as to write a series of letters on the situation to R. G. Sproul, who in 1929 was vice-president of the university:

In general view, prospects for Oceanography look dark. If Mr. K— takes Physiology into the new building Genetics and its allies will have fully half the laboratory space of the Institution (and not satisfied with that). Calling a mongrel by some high sounding name does not make him a pedigreed dog. With its mongrel characteristics it is hard to explain to some inquirers why this institution is called an Institution of Oceanography.[15]

Evidently the "allies" won out in the battle for laboratory space, for facilities for physiology were built into Ritter Hall and the department established on the building's completion in 1931. Tensions may have been eased somewhat by the fact that the same year the state legislature appropriated an additional $40,000 for the renovation and improvement of the old buildings and grounds of the institution. The old salt water system was replaced and the George H. Scripps laboratory remodelled, so that by the end of 1932 *all* the investigators were working in better facilities. In addition, space was available for about twenty-five visiting investigators. Vaughan and his staff were once again able to offer their facilities to scientists from other institutions for "virtually any kind of oceanographic research."

There was some truth in the charge that the institution had turned somewhat from its main work of oceanography if one makes the assumption, as some of the university officials and Miss Scripps' representatives evidently did, that a certain amount of first-hand observation and collecting in the open sea was essential to the institution's program. The boat work carried on by vessels either hired or owned by the institution was at a minimum during Vaughan's era, and this fact did not go unnoticed. At one point criticism of this policy prompted Vaughan to write a ten-page letter to J. C. Harper defending his position.

During Ritter's last few years as director and Vaughan's first year or two, the Scripps Institution did not own a boat capable of carrying on investigations at sea, although fishing boats were chartered from time to time. In September, 1925, the *Thaddeus*, a former purse seiner, was purchased with the funds realized from the 1917 sale of the *Alexander Agassiz*. This boat, which was renamed the *Scripps*, was 64 feet long, 22 tons register, had a 15 foot beam and 6-8 foot draft, and was equipped with an 85 horsepower gasoline engine and berths for ten. During the next few summers the *Scripps* made weekly trips to stations five and ten miles off shore, and once or twice ventured as far as San Clemente Island or the Santa Barbara Islands. In 1930, however, the boat made only five trips to the off-shore stations. "The season of 1930 represented a low ebb in the work at sea," Vaughan later conceded in a letter to J. C. Harper. "The cause was that Dr. Moberg was absent for part of the summer and then we had only a few men on the staff of the Institution who were trained in and available for the work at sea."[16]

E. G. Moberg, who was in charge of the boat work during this period, also had many duties on shore in connection with his research in chemical oceanography. It is significant, however, that he was absent in 1930 in order to help prepare reports on the oceanographic work of the non-magnetic ship *Carnegie*. He had worked aboard this research vessel of the Carnegie Institution during August and September of 1929, making observations and collections between San

Francisco and Honolulu. The value of such cooperation with other institutions and agencies was made clear in a letter which Dr. Ritter, called in as a sort of mediator during the controversy, wrote to J. C. Harper on January 21, 1931:

Concerning the boat work at the Institution, two points may be made ... (1) The possession of a boat or boats by any such institution has to be viewed in much the way that a farmer views his reaper, for instance; a necessary piece of machinery even though it must be out of use most of the time. (2) The Institution's boat work (work at sea) should be viewed as including whatever comes to the Institution from any such work. U. S. Naval ships, some passenger boats, etc., contribute largely, as you know, to this aspect of the investigations. A striking example of what this sort of thing may mean is Moberg's trip with the *Carnegie* from San Francisco to Honolulu ...

It had been expected to make even greater use of the *Carnegie*, which in 1928 had begun a worldwide cruise which was to last for three years. At the end of that cruise Dr. J. C. Merriam, director of the Carnegie Institution, was willing to turn the ship, fully equipped, over to the Scripps Institution for two years of intensive exploration in the eastern Pacific. Vaughan had already begun to look for sources for the $120,000 estimated to be necessary for two years' operating expenses, and had worked out a rather detailed plan for the projected 1931-32 cruise. In November, 1929, however, the *Carnegie* was tragically destroyed in an explosion in the harbor at Apia, Samoa, and these ambitious plans were abruptly dropped.

Nevertheless there were, as Ritter had pointed out, numerous other sources of oceanographic data available to the institution during Vaughan's administration. Due in part to his contacts in Washington, D. C., and his prominence in the leading scientific societies, Vaughan was able to greatly increase the amount of cooperation of government agencies and other scientific institutions with the Scripps Institution. In a 1931 report to J. C. Harper, Vaughan pointed out that recorded observations of ocean temperatures increased from 2170 in 1923 to 19,444 in 1925, and salinity readings from 1705 in 1923 to 5573 in 1925, which was the first year that large numbers of meteorological observations were reported to the institution. Thus those working in dynamical oceanography and meteorology had a much larger quantity of information to work with despite the fact that this information was for the most part collected by others.

Thermographs, which automatically recorded ocean temperatures, were installed on ships of the U. S. Coast and Geodetic Survey, the U. S. Navy, and even on commercial liners. Naval officers found instructions for making salinity determinations among their orders, and boxes of bottles for water samples were loaded or unloaded with the rest of the cargo. Shoreline collections by agents of the U. S. Bureau of Lighthouses had begun in Ritter's time, and this practice was expanded under Vaughan. In 1926, for example, an arrangement was made with the keeper of the Scotch Cap light station in the Aleutian Islands, who agreed to make observations for the institution in a letter which highlights some of the problems of long-distance collecting:

> Your letter dated Jan. 22nd was landed here March 15th; the mails here are very uncertain, sometimes it may be four or five months between mails, if you think it will be O.K. I am very willing to undertake the work . . . Please send full and clear instructions with the shipment, how often to take water samples, as I do not know what "Plankton" is . . .[17]

Water and plankton samples thus came from a number of sources, and arrangements were even made for the collection of marine bottom deposits.

The cooperation was not wholly one-sided. As in the case of the extra funds supplied by the Southern California light and power companies, the various agencies and institutions stood to gain from the findings of the Scripps Institution staff, and collecting data was a minor task compared to analyzing and interpreting it. The main problem from the institution's point of view, perhaps, was that the data thus assembled was limited for the most part to the main routes of trade. Knowledge of oceanic conditions along lines between major ports was considerable, but there were vast areas of the Pacific that were almost wholly unexplored. To reach these "out-of-the-way" areas the institution must have its own research vessel, and its staff would have to be willing to go to sea.

Vaughan realized that he was not the man to undertake such extensive oceanographic explorations. In 1932, already talking of retiring within the next two to four years, Vaughan wrote to R. G. Sproul, who was by then president of the University of California:

. . . I should then step out and make way for a successor who would take the lead in operations at sea. Although I am in complete sympathy with more extended operations at sea than the institution now conducts, I have passed the age at which a man should undertake the conduct of such work.[18]

Vaughan's retirement was still four years off, but finding such a successor might not be easy. It was a task which was to consume much of Vaughan's remaining time and energy, for he was fully aware that the success or failure of the Scripps Institution depended largely on its director. Gradually he had assembled a staff and acquired the laboratory facilities to carry on what he considered the most important lines of research in oceanography. What was needed now were seafaring scientists who would make the Pacific disclose the secrets of even her farthest reaches and most awesome depths.

CHAPTER XI

LOOKING SEAWARD

DURING VAUGHAN'S SEARCH for a "biological oceanographer" he had been told by Dr. Henry Bigelow, later the first director of the Woods Hole Oceanographic Institution, "There ain't no such animal in the U.S.A. You must either import him or bring him up."[1] This was indeed one of Vaughan's major problems; a number of the scientists at the Scripps Institution were engaged in research projects which did not require direct observations and collecting at sea, and making the institution one devoted to oceanography did not automatically transform its staff into oceanographers. Vaughan could hire young men competent in their particular branches of science and try to direct their attention seaward, but there was no pool of trained oceanographers from which he could draw. Nor could Europeans be lured from secure positions in their own countries by the small salaries Vaughan could afford to offer. As a result, Vaughan did what he could to "bring them up"; the Scripps Institution was the first in the country to offer a degree in oceanography.

The first student to receive a PhD in oceanography, in April, 1930, was Ancel B. Keys, who had worked mainly with F. B. Sumner and had concentrated on physiology. Others soon followed.[2] There were still many research assistants who spent time at the Scripps Institution to fulfill requirements in other departments of the university, but the La Jolla institution had at last become a department in its own right. Those working toward a degree in oceanography, although each specialized in one particular area of research, were required to know something about all aspects of oceanic investigation. Even Martin W. Johnson, who came to the staff from the University of Washington and Woods Hole in 1935 as a fully-qualified instructor in marine zoology, took McEwen's course in dynamical oceanography during his first year in order to round out his own oceanographic education.

In some of the young students Vaughan placed much of his hope for the future of the Scripps Institution and for oceanography in the United States. He was particularly gratified, in 1931, to obtain the appointment of Richard H. Fleming as a research assistant, for Fleming was the first young scientist to come to the institution with previous experience in oceanographic work at sea. After graduating with top honors in chemistry, Fleming had completed two years of graduate work, largely in biology, and had had a summer's boat work in connection with the Marine Biological Station in Nanaimo, British Columbia. He was immediately able to assist E. G. Moberg on the collecting trips of the *Scripps*, and made possible a significant increase in the institution's boat work.

Another promising young candidate for the PhD degree, who first came to the institution from the University at Berkeley as a research assistant in August, 1931, was Roger R. Revelle. Working mainly with Vaughan on the study of marine bottom deposits, Revelle soon showed a willingness and competence for work at sea. In 1933 he spent ten days on the U. S. Coast and Geodetic survey steamer *Pioneer*, and in 1934 an even longer period aboard the *U. S. S. Bushnell*, making hydrographic observations between the Aleutian Islands and Honolulu. Richard Fleming also collected data and water samples for the institution on the same basis, spending three months aboard the naval vessel *Hannibal* in the Gulf of Panama and off the coast of Costa Rica in 1933.

Prospects for the expansion of the institution's program of oceanic exploration thus began to brighten in the last few years of Vaughan's administration. The main task now was to find the "younger man who would take the lead." Vaughan, who had put aside much of his own research to give full attention to the institution, was anxious to return to Washington and his former studies, but decided in 1932 to remain at La Jolla until mid-1936. He made this decision partly because a grant from the National Academy of Sciences enabled him to take a substantial break from the routine of dealing with the institution's problems.

Late in 1931 Vaughan was asked by the Committee on Oceanography of the NAS to prepare a report on the international aspects of oceanography. In proposing the matter to President Sproul, Chairman Frank R. Lillie wrote, "I doubt if there is any person in the world who is so well prepared to undertake the preparation of the report on international aspects, as Professor Vaughan ... It would be an exceedingly important thing for the future development of oceanography if his experience could be permanently preserved . . ."[3] Preparation of such a report would entail a long trip around the world to collect information and several months of writing up the data for publication, and the Committee on Oceanography had set aside a sizable sum of money for this purpose. On the condition that he make satisfactory arrangements for the institution's management while he was away, Vaughan was given a leave of absence by President Sproul and the regents. "There will be distinct advantages from the information that I shall gain while on my journey." Vaughan wrote to Sproul. "I shall probably see nearly all of the important oceanographers of the world, and that would be of value in considering a possible successor."[4]

Vaughan left the institution in late August, 1932, and was off the university payroll for a period of fourteen months. He had made careful arrangements regarding staff appointments, general financing and over-all program, but left the details of direction in the hands of E. G. Moberg. A large part of the responsibility, in fact if not in name, fell to Tillie Genter, who had been secretary and librarian of the Scripps Institution during Vaughan's entire administration and for a number of years during Ritter's time. Staff members remember her as a perennial "Girl Friday" who always knew where everything was, carefully budgeted the meagre funds, and virtually ran the institution in her quiet and efficient way. She and Ruth Ragan, who joined the staff shortly after Vaughan became director, were for many years the mainstays of the director's office and of the library, which by 1934 numbered over 14,000 volumes and about 30,000 reprints.

Such reliable assistance in administration again proved valuable when, less than a year after his return to full-time management of the institution's affairs, Vaughan fell ill with tuberculosis. For six months he was bedridden or confined to his home, but continued by proxy to supervise the scientific work and dictated numerous letters from his bed. By now the effort to find a suitable successor had become a full-scale operation.

A committee to advise the president of the university on the selection of the new director, with George D. Louderback of the university's geology department as chairman, was set up soon after Vaughan returned from his leave of absence. This committee consulted oceanographers all over the world, and a large number of names were suggested and considered before the final choice was made. One name, however, was mentioned more frequently than any other, and usually in superlative terms. As early as May, 1932, Vaughan asked H. B. Bigelow of the Woods Hole institution to suggest a successor and reported, "He named Sverdrup, whom I know we can not get because he holds in Norway an endowed professorship for which there are no specific duties. He has a good income and can do whatever he pleases."[5]

During the next four years Harald U. Sverdrup's name recurred again and again. Everyone seemed to agree, however, that there was little chance that this famous scientist and arctic explorer, who was, in Vaughan's estimation, "the most outstanding physical oceanographer now living of early middle age,"[6] would leave his research work in Norway for a permanent position elsewhere. There was no doubt concerning his qualifications. He had been chief scientist on the seven year Arctic expedition of the *Maud* and that of the submarine *Nautilus*, and had prepared the reports on dynamical oceanography for the *Carnegie* expedition in the Pacific and for expeditions in the Antarctic. He had served in at least an advisory capacity in the preparation of similar reports on the other great oceans. Besides being "a world leader in the study of problems of oceanic circulation,"[8] Sverdrup was broadly trained in geophysics and chemistry and reputed to be "sympathetic" with other kinds of oceanographic research. "If we could get a leader such as Sverdrup associated with some of the younger men such as Revelle and Fleming," Vaughan stated at one point, "within a very short time I think the Institution would shoot forward more rapidly than has been possible during the formative period."[9]

With prospects of obtaining Sverdrup doubtful, however, Vaughan, Louderback and the committee continued to gather information about other possible candidates. Hopes brightened when, in October, 1935, Professor Bjorn Helland-Hansen, Director of the Geophysical Institute at Bergen, Norway and one of the world's foremost oceanographers, spent several days at the Scripps Institution. He had been invited by Vaughan to go over the current program and to make suggestions for the future, and the institution provided most of the expenses for his trip. Helland-Hansen was also asked to offer an opinion as to who should be the institution's next director. In November he sent a lengthy memorandum setting forth his views on the Scripps Institution's program and policy and outlined what he considered to be its most important tasks for the future. Concerning the new director he wrote:

I don't know whether Professor McEwen or Professor Moberg would wish to take the directorship. As far as I can see, they ought to continue their present research work which they pursue with great ability and success. Amongst the young Oceanographers, I have especially noted Mr. Roger Revelle whom I regard as a coming man, but he is probably too young for such a position now. I know of nobody in America who safely may be pointed out at present . . .[10]

Helland-Hansen's most definite suggestion came in a letter to university vice-president Monroe E. Deutsch:

I am sorry I cannot at present give you definite advice except to try to get hold of Dr. Sverdrup for a few years. Sverdrup is working with me at Bergen and I see him every day. When I arrive in Bergen on December sixth, I can easily speak with him, without any obligation, of course. You shall then hear from me as soon after as possible . . .[11]

A few days after his return to Bergen, Helland-Hansen cabled Vaughan "Sverdrup willing consider position according proposal,"[12] and Vaughan relayed the message to Berkeley. Although Louderback and the Committee were "very greatly pleased" by this news they made no immediate move to obtain Sverdrup's services, explaining that President Sproul was "very anxious that all possibilities be thoroughly canvassed."[13] The last few months of Vaughan's directorship were filled with a flurry of correspondence concerning a large number of candidates, but through it all, Sverdrup remained the favorite. In April, 1936, he was finally, officially asked to become the new director of the Scripps Institution of Oceanography. Fortunately the delay had not affected his earlier interest, and Sverdrup agreed to take the directorship for an initial period of three years. There was a certain amount of reservation, however, in the letter of acceptance he sent to Vaughan:

I must confess that I have hesitated in assuming the responsibility which the directorship of a great institution like Scripps must involve.

My hesitation is, I believe, rooted in my deep respect for scientific research. I have, until now, mostly attacked problems which have presented themselves to me during my somewhat varied career within geophysics, but there is a vast difference between this, I will call it personal responsibility within science, and the responsibility towards others, towards the University, the Institution and the men of science at the Institution, which the director must assume. It does not worry me that I am not an expert within many of the branches of oceanography which are represented at the Scripps Institution, since it is impossible to find anyone who would have such qualifications, but I do not want to disappoint those who think me able to carry your plans further . . .[14]

Sverdrup arrived in La Jolla in late August and spent a week going over the details of the institution's program with Vaughan. On September 1, 1936, he assumed full responsibility for the direction of that program, and it soon became evident that there would be some changes. He spent a number of hours during his first week as director visiting the local members of the Advisory Board Vaughan had set up in 1928. His main purpose in making these visits was to discover how J. C. Harper, Julius Wangenheim, Fred Baker and others who had taken an active interest in the affairs of the institution would react to the proposal of obtaining a "special vessel" for extended operations at sea. Sverdrup lost no time in "taking the lead" toward an increase in the institution's boatwork.

Meanwhile the *Scripps* was used for short trips off the Southern California coast, visiting a total of twenty-two stations in the next two months. Sverdrup asked each of the staff members to make a statement regarding the value of both extended use of the *Scripps* and, hypothetically, a larger and more fully-equipped ship, to his particular research. An immediate problem brought to his attention in this inquiry was that, as there was no special crew for the *Scripps,* those who would benefit from more frequent collecting had to enlist their scientific colleagues as crew members, often taking the latter away from more pressing work. Thus there had been an understandable hesitancy on the part of the biologists, for example, to make heavier demands on the time of those working in fields where there was less need for regular collection and observation. Hiring a part-time crew had proven difficult in the San Diego area, with the result that the non-scientific crew of the *Scripps* consisted only of the captain, Murdock G. Ross, and Henry Ball, whose services as cook were furnished under the Works Progress Administration of the federal government. These two men lived aboard the *Scripps* in her berth at the San Diego Yacht Club, and were in charge of her general maintenance and security.

On November 13, 1936, a tragic and mysterious explosion occurred on the *Scripps* as she lay at her moorings in the yacht basin, and Ross and Ball were critically burned. Ball died of his injuries a week later, and Ross never fully recovered. The Scripps burned and sank within minutes after the explosion, and as both victims were too badly injured to explain at the time, the cause of the accident remained a mystery until the boat was salvaged. The original gasoline engine had been replaced by a Diesel engine a few months before, and it was found that it had been the only gasoline equipment remaining aboard, a small stove in the galley, which had produced the blast. One theory was that Ball had looked for a leak in the connection between the stove and its supply tank with a lighted match. In any event, the *Scripps* was so badly damaged as to make her useless for further research work, though the wrecked hull was eventually patched up enough to see some service as a garbage scow in the San Diego harbor.[16] Some of the scientific equipment was reclaimed, but nevertheless, three months after he came to the institution, Sverdrup found himself without any vessel whatsoever for conducting research at sea.

If the loss of the *Scripps* had not occurred under such tragic circumstances it could almost have been considered an advantage, for the ship had been inadequate for the kind of investigations Sverdrup was contemplating. Obviously an institution of oceanography required some sort of research vessel, and no longer could anyone suggest that the staff "manage as best they could" with the *Scripps*. Sverdrup immediately began looking at available ships, taking careful notes on their potential for scientific work, and he and other staff members took short trial runs on some of them. It was even suggested that the U. S. Navy might finance the building of a completely new research ship in exchange for the privileges of using her and having access to the findings of the Scripps staff.

Early in 1937 Sverdrup arranged meetings between himself, President Sproul and Robert P. Scripps. The inheritor of the large part of his father's fortune, Bob Scripps also seemed to have inherited E. W.'s love for the sea and ships, and was himself an ardent yachtsman. He had offered the use of his own yacht, the *Novia Del Mar*, before the explosion on the *Scripps*, and Sverdrup, Moberg and Fleming had taken her out on a very successful trial voyage only a month after Sverdrup had become director of the institution. With some small modifications the *Novia Del Mar* would have been useful for longer trips to supplement the work of the *Scripps*, but her use as the institution's sole research vessel would have been incompatible with her continued use as a pleasure craft. Thus Bob Scripps agreed to purchase and refit another ship specifically for the scientific purposes of the Scripps Institution. On April 5, 1937, he bought the "luxury yacht" *Serena* from Hollywood actor Lewis Stone, and the sleek 104-foot auxiliary schooner went into a shipyard to be made more utilitarian and stable for work at sea.

The *Serena*, which was rechristened the *E. W. Scripps*, was formally presented to the institution on December 17, 1937. Her 100-foot masts had each been shortened by 28 feet, some of her staterooms had been converted into storage and laboratory space, the Diesel engine and fuel tanks had been enlarged to provide a cruising radius of 2100 miles. Two large winches, each carrying almost four miles of cable, had been installed on deck, and a number of other changes had been made. Including the cost of remodelling, the *E. W. Scripps* represented an expenditure of approximately $50,000, and was in Sverdrup's words, "ideally suited for the purposes of the institution." She was large enough to make cruises of any desired extent, but not so large that the costs of her maintenance and operation were prohibitively expensive.

Nevertheless, the regular use of a large research vessel would make necessary a considerable addition to the institution's income, and finding such additional funds would not be easy. The statewide university was still feeling the effects of the Depression, and regardless of a rapidly increasing enrollment, was struggling in 1937 and 1938 to keep within a budget that was more than a million dollars less than that of the last normal biennium ending in 1931. Robert Scripps, taking a renewed interest in the institution's affairs, agreed to contribute $15,700 toward the "professional budget and general maintenance" of the institution, and up to half of the cost of operating the *E. W. Scripps* for the year 1938-39, provided the state would match these sums. This bright financial picture darkened considerably when Scripps suddenly died of an internal hemorrhage aboard his yacht *Novia Del Mar* off the Baja California coast on March 3, 1938. He was only forty-two, and his death was wholly unexpected. Although the Ellen Browning Scripps Foundation agreed to guarantee Robert Scripps' verbal commitment of approximately $25,200 for the coming year, it was doubtful that beyond July 1, 1939, even half of this amount would be added by the Scripps family to the regular $24,000 income from Ellen Scripps' endowment. "It is sincerely hoped that the budget of the Scripps Institution can be retained at such a level that continued operation of the *E. W. Scripps* will be possible," Sverdrup concluded in his 1938 report to President Sproul, "since in oceanography work at sea is of the same importance as the work in the laboratories."

The time when such pleas for additional funds might have fallen on deaf ears among the university administration was long past. The Scripps Institution had shown itself to be a worthy member of the University of California family, and it is evident from official correspondence and actions that the needs of the institution received full consideration. Robert B. Sproul, who was president of the university for a 28-year period beginning in 1930, often visited the institution on his trips to the southern campuses, and met frequently with the director of the Scripps Institution and its chief private supporters. During these last years of the Depression, however, it had become more and more difficult to squeeze out extra funds, and every effort was made to tap outside sources of income. The Federal Bureau of Fisheries and the Geological Society of America both helped finance cruises of the *E. W. Scripps* in the late thirties.

There were beneficial as well as harmful effects of the Depression years, however, particularly in the real boost given to the Scripps Institution by workers provided by the national Works Progress Administration and the State Emergency Relief Administration. The W. P. A. undertook several projects involving manual labor at the institution in the last years of Vaughan's administration. These included road making and repairs, painting and repairs to the pier, the painting of twenty of the institution's cottages and the taking of erosion prevention measures on a large part of the institution's land. These were short term projects which required supervision on the part of the institution staff and a considerable amount of paper work, but made it possible with outside financing to meet some of the most pressing needs in the care of the buildings and grounds.

Even greater help was given by skilled and semi-skilled workers assigned to the institution by the W. P. A. and S. E. R. A. From 1934 for a period of several years the services of a large number of trained personnel, sometimes as many as twenty-five, were provided by public funds. Among these workers were translators, stenographers and typists, laboratory assistants, computers, draftsmen, photographers and librarians. With this extra help it was possible in almost every department to catch up on some of the backlog of routine analyses and calculations which had in almost every case piled up because of a lack of manpower. Under the direction of librarian Ruth Ragan the library was recatalogued, and translations of important scientific works were added to its shelves by, among others, an otherwise unemployed German baron. Some of the scientific assistants had had years of training and experience in work related to the institution's research program, and were able to carry out complicated tasks in the various laboratories. Thus despite the meagre income of the Depression, the institution benefited greatly from an expanded work force, and much was accomplished which might have had to have been postponed for many years.

With the impetus given it by the gift of a more adequate research vessel and a sizable increase in staff, the research program of the Scripps Institution made rapid progress in the late thirties. There was, however, at least in Sverdrup's view, much to be desired in the institution's program of instruction. It was difficult to find qualified graduate students to undertake the course in oceanography because of deficiencies in their college training, and Sverdrup felt that to remedy this situation it was necessary to interest students in oceanography at the undergraduate level. An awareness of the scope of the science of oceanography, and of the background in a number of disciplines which its study required, would hopefully result in a greater number of applicants adequately prepared to enter the field on the graduate level. Thus in 1937 Sverdrup and several other staff members instituted the first undergraduate course in oceanography at the Scripps Institution as part of the summer session of the University of California at Los Angeles. Attendance was small and the course was discontinued after one year, although beginning in 1939 courses in oceanography, taught by members of the institution staff, were offered in alternate semesters on the U. C. L. A. campus.

Meanwhile from eight to twelve graduate students, some of them working toward degrees in oceanography and others for degrees in departments with which the institution cooperated, continued to work and study each year at the Scripps Institution.[17] Spending half their time as research assistants in their various fields, these students also received instruction in the form of conferences and reading assignments. In addition, a weekly seminar was conducted during which the faculty members rotated in presenting results of their work or reviewing literature in their special fields. This exposure to the whole realm of oceanography was somewhat haphazard in that it depended on the special interests and method of presentation of the staff members who happened to be engaged in research at the institution. Not all fields were always adequately covered in a course of this nature, and Sverdrup and some of his colleagues felt a need for some kind of standardization.

Their efforts to set up a general course in oceanography and to define its curriculum led Sverdrup, chemical oceanographer Richard Fleming and marine biologist Martin W. Johnson, prompted by a suggestion from the representative of a New York publishing firm, to write a general textbook on oceanography. They began work on this book late in 1938, and Sverdrup stated in his annual report of 1940 that he hoped the book would appear by the end of that year or early in 1941.

None of the authors had foreseen the magnitude of the task they had assigned themselves. Originally planned to be about 420 pages in length, the textbook had grown to almost 1100 pages by the time it was published as *The Oceans, Their Physics, Chemistry and General Biology*, late in 1942.[18]

Sverdrup, who wrote fluently and prolifically in three languages, evidently had large measures of self-discipline and energy, impressing his associates with his ability to do vast amounts of work in relatively short periods of time. His co-author Richard Fleming recalls that Sverdrup began his chapters of *The Oceans* while waiting for the *E. W. Scripps*, which he was to join on a cruise, in the Mexican seaport of Guaymas. An unexpected delay, which to others might have been time wasted, was to Sverdrup a chance to work on one of his many projects.

Sverdrup arranged to join many of the cruises of the *E. W. Scripps* for short periods of time, at least, for he considered these expeditions to be the most important part of the institution's program. He summed up this feeling in his 1940 report to President Sproul:

Since my first contact with the Scripps Institution it has been my hope to establish a closer cooperation between the different specialists on the staff and gradually to develop a research program for the Institution as such. The possibility for development of an Institution program presented itself when the late Mr. R. P. Scripps in December, 1937, donated the research vessel *E. W. Scripps* to the University. With an adequate research vessel the work at sea could be planned according to problems as we see them, whereas work at sea based only on cooperation with other organizations could never become satisfactory because other wishes than ours would enter when planning cruises ... During the past biennium definite progress has been made in the concerted attack on well-defined oceanographic problems and it is hoped that further developments will follow similar lines.

Less than two years after this was written the Scripps Institution and the nation were involved in the Second World War, and long range plans gave way to immediate needs. The war brought great changes to the institution, and Sverdrup's visions of a rather modest, well-defined and unified institutional program were never to become reality. To understand the changes that occurred in the Scripps Institution during the war, however, it is necessary to understand what the institution had become under Sverdrup's leadership. The importance of the early cruises of the *E. W. Scripps*, and of some of the findings which resulted from them, was to become more and more evident as the theories were applied to practice.

CHAPTER XII

OCEANOGRAPHY AFLOAT

DUE LARGELY to the restrictive financial situation created by the Depression, the permanent staff of the Scripps Institution had remained quite small during the thirties. Despite a number of graduate student assistants and W. P. A. workers, most "departments" consisted of only one full-time, fully-qualified scientist, and naturally in some cases that scientist had gradually been led away from research in the broadest, more institutional, aspects of his field. Sverdrup found that at least half of his faculty were concerned with problems which, though somewhat related to it, were actually outside the main institutional task of obtaining a comprehensive view of the Pacific Ocean.

In addition it must have surprised Sverdrup, who came from a country where the ocean was a part of life and its study of universal concern, to discover a fair number of "landlubbers" among his staff. Several of the scientists had not been to sea for many years, and contemplated no researches that would take them there. Others could be pressed into service for short cruises, but were working on problems which depended on laboratory rather than field observations, and were for this reason not enthusiastic about work at sea. Thus Sverdrup was left with only a handful of people ready to carry out what he, in the tradition of Ritter, considered to be the institution's primary task—making a systematic physical, chemical and biological survey of the waters adjacent to the coast of Southern California.

From the European point of view the word "oceanography" was something of a misnomer in the case of the Scripps Institution, for in the Scandinavian countries, at least, the term was applied only to the study of the physics (and the chemistry as related to this) of the oceans. "I would have preferred that our name had been Scripps

Institution of Marine Sciences," Sverdrup noted at an early staff meeting, "which would better describe the activities."[1]

But as it was "out of the question to undertake any change," Sverdrup set about weaving the diverse threads of the program into a somewhat more unified whole. The central thread, he believed, must be the institution's use of its own research vessel, and when the E. W. Scripps was obtained, late in 1937, he felt that a much more integrated program was possible. In his 1940 report to the president of the university, Sverdrup summed up the first two years of this program centered around research work at sea. He described the cruises which had been planned for and undertaken by the E. W. Scripps, and the kind of information assembled during these two years, concluding:

The study of these data requires the complete cooperation of specialists in physical and chemical oceanography and of those working with phytoplankton and zooplankton. It is as yet too early to express an opinion as to the results which may be obtained from the consecutive cruises of this spring, but the preliminary work has already resulted in certain gratifying results which illustrate the value of the cooperation.

There were still some mavericks who were striking out more or less in their own directions, but Sverdrup had hopes even for some of these;

... Several staff members have continued projects which have been in progress over a period of years, some of which are independent in their nature, others of which deal with questions which sooner or later will find their places in the common program. Of the latter I wish particularly to mention Mr. ZoBell's studies in bacteriology which have fundamental bearing on the entire question of the cycle of organic matter in the sea, and Mr. Fox's studies in the biochemistry of marine organisms. Among the former I mention Mr. Sumner's work on the physiology of fishes, Mr. McEwen's studies of the interrelation between the ocean and the atmosphere and possible application to long-range weather-forecasting problems, Mr. Revelle's work in the field of sedimentation and submarine geology . . .[2]

Despite such "digressions," Sverdrup felt by 1940 that the institutional program was well underway. The E. W. Scripps, which actually began work in January, 1938, could be used either for exploratory cruises extending over some of the large unknown areas of the Pacific

Ocean or for intensive work in a smaller region. Sverdrup and his associates selected the latter alternative to begin with, because in an intensive study of a small area observations in physical and chemical oceanography and collections of biological material could be conducted on the same cruise. Such ventures were of necessity more "cooperative," and the data thus accumulated from various fields would give a rather complete picture of the area studied.

The work of 1938 and 1939 was, in Sverdrup's view, of a "preliminary nature." By making cruises off the coast of southern California in alternate months of 1938 and by completing a long cruise extending from the Oregon border to Cedros Island off Baja California in 1939, the Scripps Institution obtained a fair knowledge of the character of the waters, the type of currents, the dominating populations, and the more outstanding annual changes within the sea off their own coast. By the fall of 1939 they felt they had enough of such preliminary information to plan more intensive cruises. Accordingly, during the spring of 1940, between March 6 and June 8, the *E. W. Scripps* completed six cruises in rapid succession, each of these covering an area between San Diego and the Channel Islands and extending to a distance of about 140 miles from the coast. "We have procured a series of consecutive pictures of the currents and water masses within the area which had been selected and also of the characteristic populations of microscopic plants and smaller animals," Sverdrup explained in his 1940 report. "By comparing these pictures we shall be able to follow the changes which took place from one cruise to another."

The analysis of the data from these consecutive cruises was, in some cases, still in progress when a similar series of cruises was undertaken the following year. A longer time interval was allowed between the 1941 cruises, so that short trips for special purposes might be made between the six standard cruises to established stations. Not all of these time schedules or even specific locations of stations had been geared solely to the needs of the Scripps Institution. Both the 1940 and 1941 sets of intensive cruises were carried out in cooperation with the United States Bureau of Fisheries, which was investigating problems related to the sardine fisheries. The *E. W. Scripps* was already equipped with most of the apparatus necessary to study the distribution of sardine eggs off the California coast, and beginning in the spring of 1939, the chief of the western division of the Bureau arranged to charter her for specific periods of time. The arrangement was mutually advantageous; in urging the president's office to approve these cooperative investigations Sverdrup wrote:

I wish to recommend that the *E. W. Scripps* is chartered to the Department of the Interior on the conditions which have been mentioned because the work which is contemplated by the Bureau of Fisheries will by no means interfere with the program of the Scripps Institution, but will to the contrary supplement investigations which have been planned here. The charter sum will represent a welcome addition to the limited funds for operation of the vessel and will make it possible for the Scripps Institution to conduct its work at sea over nearly twice as long a period as would be possible if such arrangements were not made.[3]

Important results were obtained. In reporting the outcome of the 1940 cruises, Sverdrup stated that "a definite relationship was established between the ocean currents, the character of the water masses, and the regions of maximum spawning of the sardines," and that "the distribution of sardine larvae corresponded closely to what could be predicted on the basis of the computed currents." This report was written while the 1941 cruises were in progress, before any definite conclusions were possible, but so far the previously established relationships were holding true. "There are good prospects," Sverdrup concluded, "that the factors which influence the success of spawning may be recognized and that ultimately predictions as to the size of the commercially valuable stock of sardines may be prepared . . ."[4]

On most of these "cooperative cruises" of 1940-41 only one or two representatives of the Scripps Institution, often research assistants entrusted with making observations and collecting water samples, were included among the scientists on board. Earlier cruises off the California coast had drawn more heavily on the institution staff, with faculty members taking turns directing the cruises and several scientists and assistants making each trip. This intensive work in a small area, however, tended to become more or less routine, as repetition of stations visited and kinds of observations made was a definite part of the program, and many of the most important determinations and calculations were carried out on shore. There were certain cruises during this period, however, which involved a large percentage of the Scripps Institution staff and which were far from routine. Newspaper accounts at the time made them sound more like voyages of adventure and discovery than carefully-plotted scientific investigations, and even the most official reports reflect the excitement of exploring the unexplored. Two of the most important cruises of this type went to the Gulf of California, and, since in some ways they inaugurated a new era in the research of the Scripps Institution, merit a more detailed examination.

The first expedition to the Gulf of California took place early in 1939. Its main object was to study the hydrography of the Gulf and the exchange of water between the Gulf and the adjacent part of the Pacific Ocean. "We hope that knowledge of the Gulf currents ultimately will aid in the complete study of Pacific currents," Sverdrup told a reporter for the San Diego *Sun*. "From knowledge of the major currents on the coast we hope some day to be able to predict not only changes in the currents themselves, but also their effect on weather and fish migrations."[5] This cruise to the Gulf of California was thus an integral part of the institution's program, although in both methods and subjects studied there were some innovations.

Leaving San Diego on February 5, the *E. W. Scripps* proceeded to Cape San Lucas at the tip of the Baja California peninsula under sail, conserving her fuel for the runs she would make back and forth across the Gulf. Six of the fourteen persons on board were crew and six were scientists who participated in the actual exploration of the Gulf. The other two, graduate students in botany from UCLA, were "abandoned" on Cedros Island off the west coast of the peninsula to be picked up on the return trip. The two young men camped and collected botanical specimens for almost six weeks on this isolated island before they once again sighted the sails of the *E. W. Scripps*.

Two other representatives from UCLA were part of the scientific staff. One, Dr. Loye Miller, who was ornithologist on the expedition, had been a student during the summer sessions at the Coronado boathouse in the days of the institution's infancy, and had long maintained his contacts with the "station." The UCLA geology department sent a graduate student to study paleontology and living mollusca. Richard Fleming, Martin Johnson, Eric Moberg and Roger Revelle made up the contingent from the Scripps Institution staff, and Sverdrup journeyed overland to Guaymas to join the cruise for a week in early March during the exploration of the inner portion of the Gulf.

A series of lines of oceanographic stations was run across the Gulf, and over 2500 soundings were made. Water samples and samples of bottom deposits were taken at approximately fifty stations, and collections of biological material were made at both the offshore stations and certain locations on the coast. It had been necessary to obtain from the Mexican government a variety of permits, covering everything from harbor privileges to shooting specimens of birds. In case they ran up against any officials who had not been informed of the *E. W. Scripps* and her mission, the party also carried a letter in Spanish from the President of the University of California, complete with a gold seal and a brief explanation of the *E. W. Scripps'* mysterious activities.

The 1939 expedition of the Scripps Institution was the first complete oceanographic survey of the Gulf of California ever undertaken, and exploded a number of "myths." The great number of soundings showed that instead of being a broad, gently sloping depression on the earth's crust, as had been indicated on published maps, the floor of the southern part of the Gulf actually contained a series of steep ridges and deep basins and troughs. What had been reported by fishermen as "patches of oil," possibly indicating undersea oil pools, turned out to be nothing but huge masses of one-celled organisms floating on the surface of the water. One-celled animals were also shown to be responsible for the red color of the water in much of the Gulf. This coloring, which was so widespread and pronounced that it had led the Spaniards to refer to the Gulf as "the Vermillion Sea," had formerly been assumed to be due to the silt brought in by the Colorado River. The scientists took delight in disproving one other widely-accepted belief on their return from the Gulf cruise. The infamous Seri Indians of Tiburon Island, they reported, were no longer, if they ever had been, cannibals.

The waters of the Gulf of California proved to be extremely rich in organic material—from vast fields of "ocean pasturage" to huge whale sharks and manta rays. Findings indicated that this phenomenon was due to a combination of factors which brought to the surface deep water rich in mineral nutrients. In the winter strong northerly winds pushed the surface layers to the South, causing upwelling which was most pronounced in the northern part of the Gulf, and vertical mixing due to changes in the density of the surface layers caused by evaporation and cooling also played an important part in the process. Sverdrup suggested that the picture was further complicated by the presence of internal waves in the southern portion of the Gulf, and the following year a graduate student at the institution, Walter Munk, made this problem the subject of his master's thesis at the California Institute of Technology.

Important work was also done on the sediments brought up from the floor of the Gulf. An effective coring apparatus developed only a few months earlier was able to take cores of bottom mud up to nine feet in length. These cores ranged in appearance from stiff, brownish-grey clay taken near the mouth of the Colorado River to loose, flocculent green mud smelling strongly of hydrogen sulfide gas taken in the southern half of the Gulf. According to geologist Roger Revelle, the character of the sediments was a "surprise," and posed some interesting problems in the sedimentational forces operating in the Gulf. He was able to obtain a grant of $2500 from the Geological Society of America to conduct a follow-up cruise to the Gulf in the fall of 1940, which was limited solely to geological investigations.

Despite the fact that Sverdrup considered it somewhat extraneous to the main program of the Scripps Institution, the field of submarine geology made rapid advances in these early years of his administration. Almost as soon as the *E. W. Scripps* went into service, in January, 1938, she was made available in alternate months to Dr. Francis Shepard of the University of Illinois, who had been given a grant of $10,000 by the Geological Society of America to conduct studies in submarine geology off the coast of Southern California. For the duration of these studies Dr. Shepard was appointed a research associate at the institution. It was his assistants[6] from the University of Illinois who developed a heavily-weighted coring apparatus, with a specially-designed nose, which was capable of taking cores ten or more feet long. These cores of bottom sediments could be removed in an undisturbed condition by the use of open linings of galvanized metal or, later, of celluloid.

Facilitating such improvements in equipment was the workshop which Sverdrup had set up soon after his arrival at the institution. Up to that time the scientists had either had to order standard equipment, which was not always satisfactory for their specific needs, or had found it necessary to have instruments made to specification by commercial firms at much higher prices. The workshop and its able technician, Carl Johnson, afforded more flexibility and specialization, as well as being much more economical in the long run. Another device of value in the geological studies, designed by Revelle and Carl Johnson, was a current meter which could accurately measure bottom currents in water at least 1000 meters in depth from an unanchored ship. As currents close to the bottom were particularly important in the process of sedimentation, the instrument was widely used in the geological studies of Revelle and Shepard.

Shepard's main concern was the topography of the ocean floor, particularly in regard to submarine canyons, and great numbers of soundings were taken in investigating such canyons along the coast. Shepard finished his G. S. A.-backed research at the end of 1938, but returned to the institution in the fall of 1940 to take part in the second cruise to the Gulf of California. The general purpose of this expedition was to study, through a coordinated investigation of the recent geologic history of the land, of the bottom topography and sediments, and of the nature of the marine environment, the geologic processes which were or had been active in the Gulf of California. As in the case of the earlier cruise, the scientific staff was drawn from several institutions, including the University at Berkeley and UCLA as well as the University of Illinois and the Scripps Institution.[7]

The reports on the findings of this expedition, which normally would have been submitted to the Geological Society by the end of 1941, were actually not completed for several years. Revelle was called to active service in the U. S. Navy in July of 1941, and world events soon became the determining factor in the institution's program and plans. The *E. W. Scripps* was sent on her last "civilian cruise" on July 21, 1941, and was then placed at the disposal of a project at the Navy's Radio and Sound Laboratory in San Diego. The ship would remain attached to the institution but would conduct research solely of "a national defense nature" under the general supervision of the Scripps Institution director.

Sverdrup's original three-year leave of absence from the Institute of Geophysics in Bergen had been extended for two years in 1939, but he had planned to return to Norway in 1941. With the invasion of his own country and the increasing involvement of the United States in the war, Sverdrup had been forced to reevaluate his earlier decision, and on May 1, 1940, informed President Sproul that he would for the time being remain as director of the Scripps Institution. With the majority of his family and friends still in Norway, it must not have been an easy decision to make:

Regardless of what happens in the near future, and regardless of the ultimate outcome of the war, Norway will be economically ruined and will have to face a long period of reconstruction. Scientific activity will suffer because all efforts will have to be concentrated upon providing the needs of daily life. My ability and training are not of such nature that I can hope to render active help during such a period. If I returned to Norway I should become a liability because whatever place I should be able to take could be filled much better by other persons. In view of these circumstances I feel that my place is here where I may hope to contribute my share toward the further development of research activities.[8]

He was to contribute more than his share to that research and to the Allies' ultimate victory.

CHAPTER XIII

WAR, WAVES, AND REVERBERATIONS

THE NEED FOR trained oceanographers became apparent early in the Second World War. Roger Revelle, who had been called to active duty in the Navy in July of 1941, spent a short time at the Radio and Sound Laboratory on Point Loma, but was soon sent to Washington to organize and direct an oceanographic section under the Navy's Bureau of Ships.[1] As others with experience in Oceanography entered active service they were added to this small official staff, but the handful of adequately-trained personnel could never be more than a nucleus for organization. The armed forces would have found it impossible to meet the overwhelming need for knowledge of oceanic conditions created by the war had it not been for the existing oceanographic institutions and their willingness to cooperate.

Midway through 1941 a research project was set up under the direction of the University of California by the National Defense Research Council to conduct research and development in subsurface warfare. Soon designated the University of California Division of War Research and operating in facilities made available by the Navy at its Radio and Sound Laboratory on Point Loma, this project drew on the resources of the Scripps Institution, both in experience and equipment, from the beginning. Richard Fleming and Eugene C. LaFond, who had spent a number of years at the institution, were given leaves of absence on July 1, 1941, to devote their full energies to the UCDWR program. Six others who had been trained at the Scripps Institution were among the first employees of the project's division of oceanography, and additional SIO staff members were called in later when the need for their specific services arose.

The main purpose of this civilian operation, which was first directed by UCLA's Vern O. Knudsen, was to investigate methods of submarine detection and to carry on basic research on all aspects of

the oceanic environment as it related to submarine warfare. Originally it had been planned to expand the Navy's Radio and Sound
Laboratory to carry on this research, but as the civilian project came
to involve more and more people (at one time nearly 600 people were
working for UCDWR), the small Navy installation became the liaison between the huge research project and the Navy's application and
dissemination of its results in the field of operations.

The *E. W. Scripps* had been turned over to UCDWR as soon as the
project was established, and other small ships were provided by the
Navy and outfitted for oceanographic work during the course of the
investigations. Although the scientists experimented with various
types of radiation and even powerful underwater lights as possible
means of submarine detection, efforts were eventually concentrated
on sonar (from SOund, NAvigation, Ranging) techniques.
UCDWR's program was threefold: (1) the compiling of information
on sound and all aspects of the ocean—temperatures, currents, chemical properties, bottom topography, etc.—which might have some
bearing on the behavior of underwater sound; (2) the development
of offensive and defensive equipment for submarine warfare; and (3)
the selection and training of Navy personnel to operate these sensitive instruments.

Well-known scientists were drawn from many parts of the country
to conduct this research, and those with wide experience in purely
theoretical physics found themselves confronted with wholly new
problems as they tried to interpret the complex workings of nature.
Submarine detection instruments, for example, had been plagued by
a recurrent interference, a kind of rapid-fire crackling noise, under
what seemed to be completely variable circumstances regarding time
and location. Every conceivable cause was investigated, but the
experts in underwater acoustics remained completely baffled. Finally
marine zoologist Martin Johnson was called in, and he proceeded to
collect various marine animals and listen to them, at the same time
attempting to reconcile data on the location of the occurrences of this
interference with his own knowledge of the habitat of likely animal
culprits. At last he assembled enough "snapping shrimp," each
capable of making a sharp little cracking noise by snapping shut its
oversize foreclaw, to produce a facsimile of the recorded interference.
Before long the picture became complete; it was found that the
interference actually occurred only at certain depths and in proxim-

ity to the rocky bottoms where these shrimp lived. Submarine geologist Francis Shepard joined the investigations to contribute his knowledge of bottom topography, and it became possible to predict where the crackling interference would occur, and eventually to use this noise in concealing U. S. submarines. Under cover of the snapping shrimp and other predictable camouflage, U. S. submarines were able to slip undetected even into enemy harbors, and sonar operators no longer had to worry about the mysterious noise. Johnson also helped ascertain that another puzzling phenomenon, the "deep scattering layer"[2] which reflected the sonar "ping" and led to "false bottoms" or inaccurate echo soundings, had a biological cause. Physicists who had thought they could depend on sound traveling a given distance in a given length of time were surprised to find themselves contending with the whims of microorganisms and fishes.

The basic research which had been carried on at the Scripps Institution since its inception proved valuable in many ways to the work of UCDWR and the entire war effort. It was impossible to predict which findings might someday have application, and a limited amount of research not directly related to national defense was carried on at the Scripps Institution during the war. One aspect of this, C. E. ZoBell's work on petroleum-producing bacteria, was actually greatly expanded after 1940 due to large grants from the American Petroleum Institute. For the most part, however, the various departments suffered from a lack of manpower and inadequate finances. The WPA project had ended with the outbreak of the war, and graduate assistants had for the most part volunteered to serve with the armed forces. A few of the "old timers," including W. E. Allen, who retired in 1943 although he continued to work part-time for several years, and F. B. Sumner, who died in 1945 after his semi-retirement at the end of 1944, went on with their prewar research projects, but on the whole the routine was considerably interrupted.

Sverdrup himself devoted almost his full time to war-related research. When UCDWR was set up he immediately became involved, spending at least half his time at the Point Loma facilities, but this arrangement was abruptly terminated on March 4, 1942, by problems of security clearance. In his 1942 annual report Sverdrup explained that he had not been allowed to continue working with confidential information because he was not yet an American citizen, although this restriction seems to have been relaxed in a few months. Despite his temporary disengagement, Sverdrup was much too valuable a man to remain long on the sidelines.

In the summer of 1942 he was called to Washington as a special consultant to the Norwegian government, in connection with a planned invasion of Norway, because of his intimate knowledge of the waters surrounding that country. Later in the year he similarly served as an advisor to the U. S. War Department, and it was at this time that he embarked on what was to be his most important contribution to the defense effort.

A former Scripps graduate assistant, Walter Munk, who had worked closely with Sverdrup at the institution, was at this time a meteorolgist with the Army Air Corps in Washington. Asked if surf conditions during the planned Allied invasion of North Africa could be predicted in advance, Munk came to the tentative conclusion that this might be possible, and requested that Sverdrup be called in to check his findings and offer an opinion. Thus was born a wholly new science—that of surf and swell forecasting on the basis of weather maps—and when the predictions for the North African landings held true, a great burst of research activity took place at the Scripps Institution and elsewhere. Describing this hastily-assembled research project in a "Now It Can Be Told" speech after the war, Sverdrup had this to say of the problems of working under the pressure of wartime needs:

> In fairness to the academic men who participated in this and all other phases of war work, I think it should be stated that they worked under a peculiar strain because they had to carry on in a manner contrary to that to which they had been brought up and trained during their whole careers. They had been taught to check and recheck every step, to refrain from drawing conclusions on the basis of inadequate evidence, and to postpone publication of results until content and form met the most exacting standards. During the war the method of work was entirely changed. With unaccustomed responsibility it was necessary to make shortcuts, to prepare reports in record time, and to meet one deadline after another. I hope that the word deadline will forever disappear from the academic vocabulary.[3]

Sverdrup had already taught a few courses in oceanography for meteorologists to officers of the armed forces at UCLA, and in the summer of 1943, six-week courses in the new techniques of sea, swell and surf forecasting were initiated at the Scripps Institution. The tentative theories which Sverdrup and Munk had developed for the North African landings were reviewed and improved, and by the fall of 1943 were ready for distribution in mimeographed form to meteorological officers. Meanwhile research on waves being carried on at the Scripps and Woods Hole Oceanographic Institutions and at the Department of Mechanical Engineering in Berkeley found even more widespread application. Findings on the effects of shallow water bottom topography on waves led to the ability to determine underwater features such as reefs and shoals from aerial photographs of wave patterns. Many amphibious landings, particularly in the islands of the Pacific, were greatly facilitated by this development. In the first four years of the new investigations more than fifty reports were written by Scripps Institution scientists alone on various phases of the wave research. Soon after the close of the war, in a biennial report submitted to the university, Sverdrup noted that Captain H. T. Orville, Chief of the Navy's Aerological Division, had said of this work on waves that in his war experience there had been no case in which such a small investment paid such large dividends.

About two hundred Navy and Army officers completed the special courses in sea, swell and surf forecasting given at the institution, and a number of these men developed an interest in oceanography which was to last beyond the war. Several showed such an aptitude for the work on waves that they were assigned to the research and teaching group at the institution for the remainder of their military service, while still others returned as graduate students after the war.[4] Sverdrup later commented on these classes that "no two courses were the same, for new material was constantly being added and old results were simplified. The young officers who applied the new knowledge in every theater of the war deserve the greatest credit for their ingenuity and enthusiasm."[5]

With a total of fifteen of these six-week classes being held at the institution between mid-1943 and the close of the war, the SIO facilities were strained despite the cutback in regular staff. A number of technicians had been brought in to conduct special research under a contract with the Navy, and some of the laboratory and office space was devoted to this project. Under Sverdrup's supervision, extensive information on temperatures, salinity and currents of the Pacific, available to the institution through its own research and its library

facilities, was compiled and charted. This information was particularly valuable in submarine warfare, and some of the charts on currents
were printed on pocket handkerchiefs for use in air-sea rescue work.
Much of the most useful data, which had been supplied over the
years to the SIO library by Japanese oceanographers, had to be
translated before it could be charted, and translators were provided
by the Office of Strategic Services for this purpose.

Thus, although the pre-war program of the Scripps Institution had
been drastically curtailed, the buildings and grounds were full of
activity. Another laboratory was given over to research on the agar-
producing seaweed *Gelidium cartilagineum*. Conducted in cooperation with the California State Fish and Game Commission, these
studies sought less expensive ways to cultivate, harvest and extract
the vitally-needed agar, which had come principally from Japan prior
to the war. Almost all of the remaining staff members contributed in
some degree to the defense effort, in such ways as conducting independent studies of fouling organisms[6] or supplying requests for
information from the uniquely comprehensive SIO library. In response to a request from the Navy, a report was even prepared on the
feasibility of using plankton as emergency food and developing a
plankton net to be towed behind life rafts.

The wartime contributions of the Scripps Institution and its staff
members were many and varied, and found immediate application in
a number of areas. More important, however, was the fact that these
contributions demonstrated the value of basic oceanographic research
to the continuing security of the country. Some of the information
contained in Sverdrup, Johnson and Fleming's textbook *The Oceans*,
which was published in December, 1942, was considered of such vital
importance to the national interest that the book's sale was restricted
to the United States and Canada for the duration of the war.
Oceanography, which before the war had struggled to establish itself
as a respectable science, was finally and fully coming into its own.

Soon after the close of the war plans got underway for "Operation
Crossroads," the atom bomb test in the Bikini Atoll, and a number of
Scripps Institution scientists were included in these plans. One of a
large number of ships involved, the *U.S.S. Bowditch*, was to make an
oceanographic survey of the lagoon both before and after the test,
and her staff included representatives from a number of government
agencies, as well as leading scientific institutions and universities.

The leadership for this project, and the largest portion of the scientific staff, were naturally drawn from the three oceanographic institutions.[7] The *Bowditch* arrived at Bikini on March 10, 1946, well ahead of most of the task force, and made a systematic survey of the physical, biological and geological features of the lagoon and, for the purposes of comparison, of nearby Eniwetok and Rongerik Atolls. As soon as possible after the bomb was exploded the group returned to note its effect on the conditions they had observed.

Roger Revelle, as commander in charge of the oceanographic section of the Navy's Bureau of Ships, was in over-all command of the oceanographic survey, with Marston Sargent, who had been an instructor in biology at the Scripps Institution from 1937 until he was called to active duty in the Navy in 1942, in charge of the biological work. Martin Johnson was "furnished" by the institution for plankton studies, and Walter Munk for assistance in mathematical and theoretical problems of ocean diffusion. Both Sverdrup and Richard Fleming, who by that time had become assistant director of the UCDWR project at Point Loma, had given valuable assistance in making plans and procuring equipment, and a number of others who had been connected in some way with the Scripps Institution were involved in other capacities. A few of those who took part in the initial project were included in *Operation Crosscheck*, a follow-up survey of the same area conducted a year after the test.

In this and other ways the Scripps Institution and her sister institutions were able to be of assistance to the federal government, but an era had been inaugurated in which the assistance would definitely be mutual. The increased responsibilities of the oceanographic laboratories would require greatly increased funds, and there was no source large enough to provide this new income outside of the federal government. There was a certain amount of anxiety in the air in the period immediately following the war; frantic wartime activity had ceased, and pre-war programs had not yet been resumed. Columbus O'Donnell Iselin, director of the Woods Hole Oceanographic Institution, summed up this feeling of frustration and apprehension in a letter written to Sverdrup while the Bikini survey was in progress:

I will make a point of being in Washington at the time of the A.G.U. meetings. What kind of paper are you planning to give? Are you going to review the role of Scripps in the war or have you some research to report on? I have not yet made up my mind what to do. I myself have had no time for research and have nothing ready that I am at all proud of. Furthermore, it seems rather pointless to get up and review the war years. As for future plans, about all that can be said is that we have become entirely too dependent on government subsidy and that we hope they will not tie too many strings to their money. How can we operate "Atlantis" for ordinary science with sailors getting $180.00 per month and their food costing another $45.00? It has me discouraged.[8]

Even before the end of the war, meetings had been held to discuss the most reasonable ways of arranging such government subsidies and of limiting the number of attached strings, but it was some time before results could be obtained. The Navy's wartime oceanographic program had been somewhat disorganized and haphazard due to the fact that it had been set up under the pressure of immediate needs. Some contracts with civilian agencies had been arranged by the Bureau of Ships, others by the Hydrographic Office, and a few by even less related departments. After a series of conferences held at La Jolla in January of 1945, Sverdrup, Iselin, Lyman Spitzer of the National Defense Research Council and Richard Fleming recommended to Revelle, who still directed the largest part of the Navy's oceanographic program, that after the war the oceanographic unit of the Hydrographic Office be made the chief clearing house for oceanographic information and the initiator of oceanographic research. This suggestion went through the proper channels, was eventually adopted, and on May 1, 1946, Richard Fleming left his duties as assistant director of UCDWR to assume the directorship of the new Division of Oceanography under the Navy's Hydrographic Office in Washington, D. C.

Although UCDWR itself was terminated with the expiration of its Navy contract on June 30, 1946, the greater part of its program was taken over by the official naval laboratory with which it had cooperated throughout the war. Under the new title of Navy Electronics Laboratory, the military facilities were able to absorb most of those UCDWR employees who desired to stay and that part of the program, in particular, which was concerned with the development of devices for submarine detection, the training of personnel, and other of the more *applicable* features of the wartime research. It was the feeling of a number of high-ranking Navy officials, however, and of others who had been involved with UCDWR, that as extensive a research program as was necessary for real advances in knowledge of underwater sound propagation could not be carried on solely under Navy auspices. There was a need for further research, of a more fundamental nature, to be carried on "under conditions which prevail only in the universities."[9]

Early in 1946 Vice Admiral E. L. Cochran, Chief of the Bureau of Ships, proposed such a research program to University of California President Robert G. Sproul. "The wider intellectual interests involved in academic positions would attract more capable personnel to this work and would also militate against the possible stagnation of the program," he said in part. "It appears, moreover, that such a program should be of intrinsic interest to the university."[10] He thus proposed that the university enter into a contract with the Navy to continue the fundamental studies of the physics and acoustics of underwater sound started by UCDWR. The project would be established on a secure and long-range basis by the allocation of a definite fraction of the funds available to the Bureau of Ships each year for work in electronics.

As a result of this proposal and subsequent conferences, the Marine Physical Laboratory, a separate research division of the university, was set up on May 15, 1946. Its director would be Carl Eckart, who, after coming to the UCDWR project from the University of Chicago in 1942, was Associate Director in charge of fundamental research. Before coming to UCDWR Dr. Eckart had established himself as one of the leading theoretical physicists in the United States, working along with Schroedinger, Heisenberg and Sommerfeld on the development of the modern quantum theory. Later, at the University of Chicago, he had become interested in researches on the theory of irreversible thermodynamics, a subject which proved to be close to the problems which engaged his interest at the Marine Physical Laboratory. The possibility of retaining this noted physicist to direct the new research laboratory had been an important factor in the decision to establish a successor to UCDWR even before the expiration of the original contract. With ships and other facilities provided, for the most part, by the Navy Electronics Laboratory on Point Loma, the Marine Physical Laboratory was able to carry on an active research program from the outset, and also cooperated closely with the Scripps Institution of Oceanography.

Meanwhile the university was setting up similar contracts with the Navy for research to be carried on by the institution itself. On July 1, 1946, an agreement was made with the newly-established Office of Naval Research[11] providing for "research in the fields of oceanography including geographical investigations (surveys), experiments in the laboratory and at sea, theoretical studies, analysis and compilation of data and technical information, preparation of material for charts, manuals and reports, and fostering the training of military and civilian personnel"[12] under the direction of Sverdrup. There could scarcely have been fewer strings attached to this initial peacetime grant, which in practice merely provided federal funds to support the over-all program of the Scripps Institution. Partly as a continuation of a wartime contract, the Bureau of Ships gave $110,000 in October of 1946 for the development of special oceanographic instruments and the conduct of "related" oceanographic research, particularly in interpreting the data obtained in Operation Crossroads. Beginning on November 1, 1946, the Office of Naval Research also undertook to support studies on fog. The institution, already cramped for space, found it necessary to purchase two "temporary" barrack buildings at a cost of $4100, and these were moved from Camp Callan and installed on the institution grounds in time to house the new projects.[13]

After the close of the war the Ellen Scripps Foundation had resumed its contributions to the work of the institution, but the financial picture was beginning to change, and even state-provided funds were to become a much smaller percentage of the institution's income. Sverdrup attributed much of the willingness of the Navy to support oceanographic research to the efforts of Roger Revelle. "He deserves great credit for having demonstrated to the Navy units the value of oceanographic information and for arousing interest leading to the establishment of a Division of Oceanography in the Hydrographic Office, and for the plans for Navy support of oceanographic research,"[14] Sverdrup said of Revelle in his 1946 report to President Sproul. Science had ceased to be purely academic, and although university funds were needed to support, in particular, some of the biological research at the institution, even the work on plankton and fishes tapped new sources of revenue after the war.

The California sardine industry, which for a number of years had been a $65,000,000 enterprise, had suffered a severe loss in 1946. The

[146]

yearly catch of sardines off the California coast, which had been as high as 800,000 tons, soon fell as low as 150,000 tons, and the little research which had been conducted in this field was wholly inadequate to explain the sudden disappearance of the fish, referred to in the press as "The Case of the Missing Sardines."[15] In 1947 the state legislature passed a measure to provide $300,000 for the support of a greatly expanded research program, and increased the appropriation to $400,000 in 1948. In addition a tax of fifty cents per ton was levied on the sardine catch, and the revenue thus derived, which was expected to amount to almost $100,000 a year, was to help finance this intensive program of research into the causes of the diminishing supply of sardines and other studies of value to the fisheries industry. The project was statewide, and a number of organizations participated, but the bulk of the research was to be conducted by the Scripps Institution. As the Marine Life Research Program, the project was set up at the institution in 1947, and necessitated the hiring of several new staff members.

The state and industry-provided funds also enabled a significant addition to the facilities of the institution in the form of two new research vessels. A 143-foot former seagoing tug, which was rechristened the *Horizon*, and a former mine sweeper, which was 134 feet in length and renamed the *Crest*, were obtained from the Navy and extensively reconditioned and equipped for oceanographic work with a part of the Marine Life Research funds. After these ships became available in 1948, they were used exclusively for the fisheries investigations. A third ship, the *Paolina T.*, a former purse-seiner 80 feet in length, was purchased with Navy funds in July of 1948. The operating costs for the smaller ship would be drawn from the university budget, and she was to carry on research both under the institution's contract with the Navy and under the state fisheries program. This brought the SIO "fleet" to four well-equipped vessels, with the *E. W. Scripps* still being used for general oceanographic work.[16]

A great postwar expansion in oceanographic research had begun, and Harald Sverdrup played a vital role in laying the foundations for that growth. Although the war had proven the value of oceanography and insured its continued support, each separate contract had to be negotiated through countless letters and conferences, and the administrative details of budgeting and handling these funds from many sources were all but overwhelming. Gradually each research project was set up and necessary facilities and equipment were obtained. By the year 1947 appropriations from various sources to the Scripps Institution totalled $869,559.48 and the number of employees had grown to 154.[17]

It had been necessary to fill a number of vacancies on the faculty in these years just following the war. Professor Carl Hubbs, a well-known icthyologist from the University of Michigan, took the place of F. B. Sumner in 1944, and in 1946 Professor Norris W. Rakestraw came from Brown University and Woods Hole Oceanographic Institution to direct the work in chemical oceanography. Also joining the faculty were instructor David Carritt, to work with Rakestraw, and Theodore J. Walker, instructor in oceanography. There was even, after more than 30 years, a changeover in the curatorship of the museum aquarium, when Percy C. Barnhart retired and Sam Hinton, who had been Director of the Desert Museum in Palm Springs and connected with UCDWR during the war, became curator in his place.

A significant increase in the number of graduate students occurred as well. Immediately after the war Sverdrup had made plans for new courses and teaching facilities in anticipation of greater enrollment. The war and its resultant boost to oceanographic research had created a demand for trained oceanographers, and the Scripps Institution was still the only one in the country which offered a degree in the field. In 1947, 41 graduate students registered at Scripps, and Sverdrup wrote that the only limitation was that of space.[18] By the next year the state approved a half-million dollar appropriation for the improvement and expansion of the institution's facilities, including the construction of a $250,000 museum building to replace the tiny wooden aquarium and free the whole of the old museum-library for books.

In the eleven and a half years of Sverdrup's "temporary" term as director the institution had been transformed from a rather modest little research laboratory, with seven on the faculty, into a thriving and essential member of the nation's scientific aggregate, and this was only the beginning. Sverdrup himself realized that the possibilities in oceanographic research were virtually unlimited and had only begun to be explored. He further felt, however, that the leadership for the necessary expansion and innovation he foresaw should perhaps be drawn from the ranks of those young men who had grown up with the science of oceanography and had been shaped into leaders by the demands of wartime. The United States was in a position to support an even larger research program, and other men might better be able to tap these resources. Thus, when his own country asked him to return to direct its new Norwegian Polar Institute, Sverdrup could accept without feeling he was "deserting the ship." He had, after all, gotten it afloat. Nevertheless, the decision was not made easily, and his acceptance of the post in Norway was based primarily, Sverdrup explained, on his desire to "assist that small nation during a period when it is struggling to get back on its feet after five years of oppression."[19] Thus, in July of 1947, he handed in his resignation, to take effect the first part of the next year.

Sverdrup would be sincerely missed at the Scripps Institution. As evidence of their esteem and in recognition of what he had done for the institution and for oceanography, his associates published an anniversary volume of scientific papers on the occasion of Sverdrup's sixtieth birthday, a few months after he and his wife Gudrun returned to Norway. The introduction to this collection, which was written by Walter Munk and Roger Revelle, reflects the high regard accorded Sverdrup by all his staff. Entitled "Harald Ulrik Sverdrup: An Appreciation," this dedicatory introduction summarized Sverdrup's career and contributions, and said in part:

The most significant of the *Maud* papers, "Dynamics of Tides on the North Siberian Shelf," was completed for publication during the last winter in the Arctic, without adequate literature and without the benefit of discussion with colleagues. Such an accomplishment was possible only because Sverdrup had developed, to a remarkable degree, internal harmony and simplicity during the long years on the ice. These gave him an objective confidence in his own thinking and the ability to bring his thoughts to well rounded, definite conclusions. Internal harmony between the diverse aspects of a complex personality, between the explorer and the scholar, the naturalist and the theorist, the teacher and the administrator, is still Sverdrup's outstanding characteristic.

Yet the achievement during the expedition of which Sverdrup is most proud is not scientific: after seven years on the *Maud* he parted friends with his shipmates. Such a feat must have required all the humor, kindliness, insight and self-discipline which characterize him today . . .[20]

Sverdrup had been in many ways an ideal director for the Scripps Institution, and it was not easy to replace him. When he and his wife left for Norway at the end of February in 1948, the identity of his successor still had not been made public. Within a short time, however, it was announced that Carl Eckart, who had already added administrative duties to his research interests as head of the Marine Physical Laboratory, would become Director of the Scripps Institution. To simplify many matters of administration and finance the MPL was made a division of the institution at this time, and Eckart remained as director of both programs. In the summer of 1948 Roger Revelle returned from Washington to fill the newly-created post of Associate Director, and the work of the institution continued to expand under the able leadership of these two men. When Eckart resigned early in 1950 to devote his full time to his own research work, Revelle became Acting Director, and on July 1, 1951, Director of the Scripps Institution of Oceanography. Twenty years after he had come to the institution as a graduate student Revelle had returned to be its head.

One of Revelle's first undertakings as Acting Director of the institution, in the latter half of 1950, was to lead Operation Mid-Pacific, an expedition to the central Pacific between the equator and 40° North Latitude, and from the west coast of the United States to the Marshall Islands. Much of this area, lying as it did far from steamship lanes, was almost completely unexplored scientifically, and the findings of the thirty scientists and eighty-five technicians and crew members, it was expected, would comprise "a completely new level in our knowledge of the east central area of the world's largest ocean."[21] Exciting discoveries were made, including the existence of the Mid-Pacific Mountains, a tremendous underwater range, but the most important features of Operation "Midpac" were not necessarily its scientific results. It was a new type of expedition—more extensive, more costly than any the Scripps Institution had before conducted. This was made possible because Midpac was a cooperative venture, sponsored by the Institute of Geophysics of the University of California, the Office of Naval Research and the Bureau of Ships, and carried out by the Scripps Institution and the Navy Electronics Laboratory. The 220-foot *EPCE(R)*-857, assigned to NEL as a research vessel, accompanied the institution's 143-foot *Horizon,* and the scientists who participated were drawn from U.C.L.A., U.S.C., Stanford and the U. S. Geological Survey as well as from NEL and Scripps Institution.[22] With the combined resources and experience of the government and educational institutions the possibilities in oceanic exploration became virtually unlimited.

By 1950 the Scripps Institution of Oceanography was thus reaching far out into the Pacific, and in the next decade her vessels would explore its most remote areas and even venture beyond its boundaries. The little marine biological laboratory had grown, as Director Ritter had hoped it would, into "an oceanographic institution worthy of the magnitude of the problems"[23] of that great ocean. The staff and facilities of the Scripps Institution would continue to grow, and a great amount of new information, and new problems, would be uncovered by the research conducted there. "The farther one advances in experience and knowledge," Ritter had written in 1911, "the more does he become impressed with the vast scale on which things are done in the ocean and the literally infinite complexity of cause and law there in operation."[24] It was a statement which, like many of those in which Ritter had tried to capture his vision, was as true of the institution fifty years later as it had been at the time it was written. There is yet a great deal to be learned about the world's oceans.

It cannot be denied, however, that the Scripps Institution of Oceanography has made a beginning. The pueblo lot at La Jolla has been the site of some of the most significant advances in the science of the ocean in the last half-century. In part these particular events, in this particular location, may have been due to chance, but largely they have been due to people. Ritter and his ability to inspire others with his own vision and determination, Vaughan and his careful planning and important national and international connections, Sverdrup and his strong leadership in taking the work to sea, coping with the war and building up support, Revelle and his successors who have pushed the frontiers of the science beyond the others' fondest dreams —these men and those they gathered around them tell the story of the Scripps Institution. It is, in a way, the story of the gradual embodiment of what was to begin with a very big idea. Even ideas, however, though they may set goals, cannot set limits. The guiding concept has grown and changed and will continue to do so, for the Scripps Institution of Oceanography is limited only by the capacities of the men who work long hours in her laboratories and probe the farthest reaches of the sea in her ships.

EPILOGUE
SCRIPPS AS IT IS TODAY

IN ENDING THIS ACCOUNT just short of the greatest period of expansion in the rather brief history of oceanography, the authors are fully aware that much remains to be told of the Scripps Institution of Oceanography and its accomplishments. To relate in comparable detail the events of the last fifteen years the present volume would have to be at least double its present length, and still much would have to be omitted. The scope of the institution's expeditions, the diversity of its research, the ever-increasing number of its graduates —trends which have largely been established during the era of Roger Revelle, and his successors, Fred Spiess and William Nierenberg—are the story of the present as well as the recent SIO, and none is a closed chapter. "Scripps As It Is Today," and the further story of how it became what it is, would furnish the material for at least another volume. Hopefully, this may someday be written.

In the meantime the following summary is presented for purposes of comparison with those eras in the history of SIO which *are* covered in the preceding chapters, to enable the reader to see what has become of Ritter's "baby elephant." These facts and figures reflect little of the human element so important in the development of any institution. The Scripps Institution of Oceanography, whatever it is today, is a result of the ideas and efforts of individuals too numerous to list.

Administratively, Scripps is now an institution for research and graduate instruction within the University of California, San Diego, one of the newest of the university's nine campuses. UCSD, which is expected to grow to an enrollment of some 27,500 students by the year 2000, will eventually be made up of twelve undergraduate colleges and several graduate schools. The first of these, Revelle College, was opened in 1964, and John Muir College is scheduled to begin classes in 1967. The Scripps Institution was much of the attraction and provided the nucleus for this new general campus, which is located on the mesa to the north and east of the original pueblo tract.

Scripps, including the affiliated institutes of Geophysics and Planetary Physics and Marine Resources, receives approximately 17 percent of its support from the State of California, 81 percent from the federal government, and two percent from other sources, including the Scripps endowment. In the fiscal year ended June 30, 1965, total support amounted to slightly over ten million dollars. The Office of Naval Research has become the largest single source of funds for the Scripps Institution, with such federal agencies as the National Science Foundation and the Atomic Energy Commission, along with the state, making sizable contributions.

Organizationally, Scripps is divided into two teaching departments, Oceanography and Marine Biology, and cooperates closely with the Earth Sciences Department of Revelle College. Its chief research units are the Divisions of Oceanic Research, Earth Sciences, and Marine Biology, the Marine Physical Laboratory and the Visibility Laboratory. Also carrying on research projects on a more or less permanent basis are the Marine Life Research Group, the Applied Oceanography Group, and the Physiological Research Laboratory. Other research programs are set up for varying lengths of time to study specific problems, usually drawing staff members from diverse divisions within the institution.

Also located on the campus are branches of two university-wide units, the Institute of Geophysics and Planetary Physics and the Institute of Marine Resources, both of which cooperate closely with the Scripps Institution. The Institute of Marine Resources supports research within the SIO, and its director must be a member of the Scripps faculty. Cooperating with the institution in the maintenance of a radio station with worldwide coverage is the Fishery Oceanography Laboratory of the Bureau of Commercial Fisheries. This laboratory is located on land adjacent to Scripps in La Jolla, in a building which also houses the headquarters and laboratory of the Inter-American Tropical Tuna Commission and Scripps Tuna Oceanography Research, STOR.

Most of the readily accessible building sites on the original pueblo tract have been used, and future facilities will necessarily be located on the more hilly and removed sections of the institution's land. The original George H. Scripps building was enlarged in 1958 and now contains central administrative offices as well as laboratories. Substantial additions have also been made to Ritter Hall, which now has six times its original floor space for offices and laboratories. Sverdrup

Hall, a three-story structure completed in 1960, contains most of the other offices and individual laboratories at the La Jolla location.

The Thomas Wayland Vaughan Aquarium-Museum, completed in 1951, freed, as planned, the original Library for its main purpose. The Library has been remodeled, and now contains over 63,000 volumes, 87,000 reports and reprints, 3000 serials, a large collection of charts and a valuable special collection of historical oceanography. It is one of the most complete oceanographic libraries in the world.

Other permanent buildings at the La Jolla site include the Francis B. Sumner Auditorium, which was completed in 1960, and various special research facilities. These are an Experimental Aquarium, a facility for Sea Water Conversion and Core Storage, the building of the Institute of Geophysics and Planetary Physics, a Hydraulic Laboratory and a Physiological Research Laboratory. There are also a number of temporary frame buildings on the campus, including the original Director's Residence and some of the original cottages. These have been converted, for the most part, into offices and laboratories, and temporary structures also house machine and electronic shops.

Although more than half of the Scripps staff works in La Jolla, a considerable fraction is accommodated in facilities on Point Loma in or close to the buildings of the Navy Electronics Laboratory, with which the institution has maintained close working relations. The headquarters and many staff members of the Marine Physical Laboratory are located on Point Loma, as are the Visibility Laboratory and the activities of the Applied Oceanography Group. The Chester W. Nimitz Marine facility of the Scripps Institution, a ship-operating base with five new buildings including facilities for docking, maintenance and expedition staging, was completed at the beginning of 1966 on a six-acre tract leased from the Navy on Point Loma. This provides, for the first time, a single home base for the Scripps research fleet, which is the largest such fleet outside the federal government.

The Scripps Institution now operates eight ocean-going research vessels, ranging in size from the 65-foot *T-441* to the 213-foot *Argo*, as well as a number of small craft. A total of 19 ships have been operated by the institution since its beginning, the majority of these having been built for other purposes and converted for research use. The last three additions to the fleet, however, including the 95-foot *Ellen B. Scripps*, the 130- foot *Alpha Helix* and the 210-foot *Thomas*

Washington, all acquired in 1965, have been constructed specifically for oceanographic purposes.

An important part of the Scripps fleet is the 355-foot spar buoy laboratory, FLIP (for Floating Instrument Platform). Unique among the world's research craft, FLIP is towed horizontally to its station, then "flipped" into a vertical position by flooding ballast tanks. In this upright position, with 300 of its 355 feet under water, FLIP becomes a remarkably stable platform for making accurate scientific measurements at sea.

The institution has a number of other special facilities which have largely been developed to meet specific research needs. One of these is radio station WWD for ship to shore communications, operated, as mentioned previously, jointly with the Bureau of Commercial Fisheries. The 1000-foot pier constructed in 1916 still receives wide use, and the intake pipes located at its extreme end continue to provide an abundant supply of clean sea water for the laboratories. Other special facilities include an offshore underwater reserve, a large collection of deep sea sediment cores, a collection of original echogram soundings over a wide area of the Pacific and other oceans, and an oceanographic data archive of some half-million bathythermograph observations. Carbon-14 and tritium laboratories and electron microprobe and electron microscope laboratories, as well as six mass spectrographs, are also available for use. In addition, there is a large collection of sea water samples, a fish collection of more than 100,000 specimens of some 1500 marine species, and another large collection of marine invertebrates. Scripps scientists also have access to the University Computer Center.

Such specialized facilities would indicate that the institution's research activities have greatly expanded since the departure of Director Sverdrup, and such is indeed the case. The faculty and academic staff has grown from 16 in 1948 to 132, and is expected to increase. Including support staff, the total payroll numbers approximately 800 employees. The number of graduate students in 1966 is 124, and up to the present a total of 146 Ph.D. degrees have been awarded for work at the institution.

All of these people have kept busy, and it is impossible even to summarize the institution's research accomplishments in this brief outline. Since the first major expedition in 1950, Scripps ships have steamed more than 901,406 miles in long expeditions alone, and in all research activities currently log about 200,000 miles a year. In 1962-63 the *Argo* established the world's record for distance traveled in a single expedition when she broke the long-standing record of the *Challenger* expedition by logging 86,000 miles in a 15-month trip to the Indian Ocean, on Expedition Lusiad.

Meanwhile the research activity on shore goes on at an unflagging pace, constantly uncovering new problems as it adds to the store of knowledge of the world's oceans. More than 200 scientific papers and books are published by the Scripps staff each year, representing a variety and complexity of scientific work which no single individual could possibly encompass. Nor is there a foreseeable end to the growth and diversification of the Scripps research program. "The oceans are so big that no institution or country alone can find out what we need to know," Roger Revelle said in 1964. "Scripps was a pioneer in oceanography, and we still are . . . we are just approaching revolutionary knowledge."

NOTES

CHAPTER I

CAMPING AND COLLECTING

[1]Fred Baker, "Dr Ritter and the Founding of the Scripps Institution of Oceanography," *Presentation and Acceptance of a Portrait of Dr. William Emerson Ritter, First Director of the Scripps Institution, Presented by Miss Ellen Browning Scripps to the Scripps Institution of Oceanography, University of California,* Bulletin 15 (Non-Technical) of the Scripps Institution of Oceanography, University of California Press, Berkeley, January 28, 1928, p. 11.

[2]Mary Bennett Ritter, *More Than Gold in California,* 1849-1933, The Professional Press, Berkeley, 1933, p. 239.

[3]William E. Ritter, *The Marine Biological Station of San Diego: Its History, Present Conditions, Achievements, and Aims,* University of California Publications in Zoology, Vol. 9, No. 4, University of California Press, Berkeley, March 9, 1912, p. 144 (hereafter cited as *The Marine Biological Station,* 1912).

[4]The Marine Biological Laboratory at Woods Hole was established in 1888, the Stazione Zoologica on the Bay of Naples, Italy, in 1872.

[5]W. E. Ritter, "The Harriman Alaskan Expedition," *University Chronicle,* August, 1899, pp. 228-229.

[6]Benjamin Ide Wheeler to William E. Ritter, December 14, 1900. This and other letters cited are preserved in the archives of the Scripps Institution of Oceanography Library, La Jolla, California (hereafter referred to as SIO Archives).

[7]Ritter, *The Marine Biological Station,* 1912, p. 152.

[8]W. E. Ritter, "A Summer's Dredging on the Coast of Southern California," *Science* (A weekly journal devoted to the Advancement of Science, publishing the official notices and proceedings of the American Association for the Advancement of Science), January 10, 1902, pp. 55-65.

[9]"Students Seeking Marine Life," the San Diego *Union,* July 18, 1901, p. 7.

[10]Fred Baker to F. R. Burnham, January 30, 1903.

[11]Ritter's report elaborates on this: "No similar occurrence of this organism on the Pacific Coast of North America is recorded so far as I am aware. Indeed, inquiry among many old fishermen, and longshore seamen, who have been familiar with the region for many years, elicited the affirmation, in every instance, that such a thing had never before taken place within the period of their acquaintance with the coast." W. E. Ritter, "Preliminary Report to the President of the University of California on the Marine Biological Explorations Conducted by the Zoological Department of the University on the Coast of Southern California during the Summer of 1901," unpublished manuscript, SIO Archives.

[12]*Ibid.,* p. 11.

[13]Ritter to Baker, May 26, 1902.

[14]Ritter, *The Marine Biological Station,* 1912, p. 152.

CHAPTER II

THE TEMPTATIONS OF TENT CITY

[1]Dr. Fred Baker was an ear, eye, nose and throat specialist; Dr. Charlotte, a general practitioner.

[2]Baker to Ritter, May 15, 1903.

[3]Baker to Ritter, March 15, 1903.

[4]W. E. Ritter, "Report of the Marine Biological Laboratory to the Chamber of Commerce Committee," quoted in the San Diego *Union*, August 1, 1903.

[5]*Ibid.* The following people were named as members of the fund gathering committee: Dr. Fred Baker, H. P. Wood, Dr. F. R. Burnham, J. N. Newkirk. "Other benefactors" included E. W. Scripps, Miss Ellen Scripps, Homer H. Peters, Coronado Beach Company by E. S. Babcock, Manager, Mrs. Fannie Keating, U. S. Grant, Jr., George W. Marston, San Diego Electrical Company by W. E. Clayton, Manager, and H. W. Putnam.

[6]*Ibid.*

[7]Albert Britt, *Ellen Browning Scripps, Journalist and Idealist,* Printed for Scripps College at the University Press, Oxford, 1960, p. 42.

[8]Baker to Ritter, March 15, 1903.

[9]Ritter to Baker, August 22 and 23, 1903.

[10]Baker to Ritter, September 17, 1903.

[11]*Ibid.*

CHAPTER III

A DEGREE OF IMPRACTICABILITY

[1]E. W. Scripps to Baker, August 12, 1903.

[2]Governor George C. Pardee to Ritter, March 23, 1904.

[3]Wheeler and Pardee to Peters, undated letter, SIO Archives.

[4]E. W. Scripps to Ritter, March 30, 1904.

[5]Ritter to Baker, December 12, 1904.

[6]E. W. Scripps to Ritter, February 9, 1905.

[7]Ritter to Baker, December 2, 1904.

CHAPTER IV

THE LITTLE GREEN LABORATORY AT THE COVE

[1]Baker to Ritter, February 2 and 27, 1905.

[2]Resolution adopted by the Board of Regents of the University of California, February 13, 1906, official copy preserved in SIO Archives.

[3]E. W. Scripps to Mayor John L. Sehon, August 29, 1906.

[4]The story of the Loma's demise came largely from conversations with Miss Molly Baker, Dr. Fred's daughter, who, until her death in 1965, still lived on the Roseville land. Dr. Fred's home can be seen at 842 Rosecrans. Miss Baker was home from Stanford University the summer of 1906, assisting at the La Jolla station, and remembered the shipwreck clearly.

[5]Ellen B. Scripps to Charles A. Kofoid, July 30, 1906.

[6]W. E. Ritter, "The Marine Biological Association of San Diego," *Science*, September 20, 1907.

[7]Baker to Ritter, November 7, 1905.

[8]Ritter to Mayor Sehon and the San Diego City Council, January 3, 1906.

[9]E. W. Scripps to Sehon, August 22, 1906.

[10]E. W. Scripps to Sehon, August 27, 1906.

[11]Ritter to H. W. Heller, September 4, 1906.

[12]E. W. Scripps to Heller, August 22, 1906.

[13]Draft of the enabling act preserved in SIO Archives.

CHAPTER V
UNDER THE HAMMER

[1]E. W. Scripps to Mayor Sehon, August 29, 1906.

[2]Miss Ellen Scripps to Baker, May 1, 1907.

[3]Mrs. Mary B. Ritter to Baker, May 1, 1907.

[4]Miss Ellen Scripps to Baker, May 1, 1907.

[5]Baker to Ritter, October 15, 1906.

[6]C. E. Richards to Members of the Marine Biological Association, July 29, 1907.

[7]W. E. Ritter, "A Popular Lecture to the Citizens of La Jolla, July, 1907," unpublished speech, SIO Archives.

[8]Copy of resolutions drawn up by E. W. Scripps in 1907, SIO Archives.

[9]Ritter to Kofoid, June 12, 1908.

[10]W. E. Ritter, "The Scientific Work of the San Diego Marine Biological Station During the Year 1908," *Science*, September 11, 1908, pp. 329-333.

[11]Ritter to Julius Wangenheim, January 31, 1907.

[12]E. W. Scripps to Ritter, November 9, 1908.

[13]Quoted in letter from J. C. Harper to Ritter, February 25, 1909.

[14]E. W. Scripps to Ritter, February 2, 1909.

[15] E. W. Scripps to Ritter, February 25, 1909.

CHAPTER VI
THE REGENTS AND THE RANCH

[1]W. E. Ritter, *The Marine Biological Station*, 1912, p. 146-147.

[2]Ritter to C. L. Holliday, November 22, 1909.

[3]Ritter to Holliday, February 8, 1912.

[4]E. W. Scripps to Ritter, June 19, 1910.

[5]E. W. Scripps, "The Biological Station Begins to be a Disappointment," June 2, 1909, unpublished disquisition, SIO Archives.

[6]E. W. Scripps to Ritter, June 19, 1910.

[7]J. C. Harper to Ritter, July 25, 1910.

[8]Ritter to Harry L. Titus, August 8, 1910.

[9]Ellis L. Michael to Ritter, March 8, 1911.

[10]E. W. Scripps to Albert Schoonover, November 25, 1911.

[11]C. A. Kofoid to Ritter, October 20, 1911.

[12]E. W. Scripps to Schoonover, November 25, 1911.

[13]E. W. Scripps to Ritter, February 24, 1911.

[14]Ritter to President Wheeler, November 3, 1910.

[15]W. E. Ritter, *The Marine Biological Station of San Diego*, Frye and Smith, San Diego, January, 1910, p. 8.

CHAPTER VII

THE BIOLOGICAL COLONY

[1]Ralph P. Merritt to Ellen B. Scripps, July 12, 1912.

[2]J. C. Harper to Governor Hiram Johnson, March 12, 1913.

[3]Merritt to W. C. Crandall, April 11, 1913.

[4]Helen Raitt's interview with Mrs. F. B. Sumner, March 6, 1962.

[5]Mary Bennett Ritter, *More Than Gold in California*, 1849-1933, p. 302.

[6]Ritter to C. A. Kofoid, June 26, 1913.

[7]W. E. Ritter, "Scripps Institution for Biological Research," in the *Annual Report of the President of the University on behalf of the Regents to His Excellency the Governor of the State, 1913-1914* (hereafter referred to as *Annual Report*), July 1, 1914, reprint preserved in SIO Archives.

[8]Crandall to Merritt, April, 1915.

[9]Ritter, *Annual Report*, July 1, 1915.

[10]Undated newspaper clipping preserved in SIO Archives.

[11]This commons building was connected to the institution road by a long, narrow footbridge on the east. In 1963 the canyon was filled in and this area became the site of the Institute of Geophysics and Planetary Physics.

[12]Ritter to C. C. Nutting, February 8, 1915.

[13]These descriptions and much of the information concerning life at the institution during this period came from interviews by Helen Raitt with Mrs. F. B. Sumner, Mrs. W. C. Crandall, Mrs. G. F. McEwen, Dr. Myrtle Johnson, Dr. Anita Laton and Dr. Edna Watson Bailey, Dr. Ritter's literary executor.

[14]Ritter to Crandall, February 21, 1914.

[15]Crandall to Ritter, February 21, 1914.

[16]The Hannay family, who kept this farm, raised goats as well as cows and chickens. Later this area was the site of a research laboratory connected with the Scripps Metabolic Clinic in La Jolla, and large numbers of stray dogs collected on the streets of Tijuana were kept there for experimentation. In 1957 the institution's radio facilities for ship to shore communication were established in the same general location.

[17]The winding road built with Miss Scripps' 1907 donation was for a long time called the Biological Grade, then the Scripps Grade and later La Jolla Shores Drive.

[18]In October, 1916, F. B. Sumner began construction of cottages on his acre adjoining the campus on the cliff at the north. One of these was built for his mother. After Dr. Sumner's death in 1945, Mrs. Sumner disposed of the property, and two new houses were built on the acre in addition to the original Sumner house, which still stands at 9030 La Jolla Shores Drive.

P. S. Barnhart completed his building in November, 1916, on his acre on top of the hill. The family sold the house to a Mrs. Shute four years later, as they wished to move inland away from the sea breezes. A later resident, Mr. Broderick, sold gasoline for a number of years at a small station that can still be seen near the remodelled Barnhart house at 9410 La Jolla Shores Drive.

Today is seems surprising that no other staff members took advantage of E. W.'s offer. Early residents explain that at the time these acres seemed too isolated and remote.

[19]E. W.'s dream of having these forty acres used for homes by the staff of the Scripps institution came partially true much later. Attorney Smithton remembered Scripps' intention and many years after E. W.'s death, when the estate wished to sell the property, he called Dr. Walter Munk of the institution staff and gave him only twenty-four hours to raise the money to purchase the forty acres. The author and others who attended a hastily-called meeting decided that raising the required sum within the time alloted was an impossibility. The land subsequently went to a single buyer who sold eight acres soon after World War II for a number of homes on Poole Street and La Jolla Shores Drive, which today house many university people.

All but the best view acreage was sold in 1951 to the cooperative Scripps Estates Association, made up largely of institution staff members, who subdivided it among themselves for home sites. Their non-profit corporation did not allow the land to be sold at a profit to anyone, and in other ways controlled the use of the land, as had been the intention in 1916. The S.E.A. followed E. W.'s wish in naming the central road Ellentown, but houses were built on these forty acres which cost considerably more than the original $2500 limit. The first nineteen members of this association chose their building sites in a lottery, and also decided to preserve the canyon adjacent to them in its natural state.

CHAPTER VIII

OF MEN AND MICE

[1]Francis Bertody Sumner, *Life History of an American Naturalist*, The Jaques Cattell Press, Lancaster, Pennsylvania, 1945, p. 205.

[2]*Annual Report*, July 1, 1941, p. 6 (during term of Director H. U. Sverdrup).

[3]Among the artists was sculptor Arthur Putnam, protege of E. W. Scripps whose bust of the publisher was given to the institution at a later date. At one time Putnam and two other artists lived in the institution cottages. The two painters left their imprint in the form of a huge mural at the top of the museum-library stairs, depicting sea nymphs and assorted other sea creatures.

[4]Quoted in *Annual Report*, July 1, 1921.

[5]*Annual Report*, July 1, 1920.

[6]*Annual Report*, July 1, 1914.

[7]*History in the News, 1919-1933*, November 7, 1922. This is a collection of news releases preserved in the SIO Archives.

[8]Ritter to F. B. Sumner, June 20, 1913.

[9]*Annual Report*, July 1, 1912.

[10]Ritter to Sumner, June 25, 1913.

[11]*Annual Report*, (T. Wayland Vaughan, Director), July 1, 1924.

[12]Preserved in SIO Archives.

[13]*Annual Report*, July 1, 1918.

[14]Much later the San Diego *Union*, on September 12, 1960, told the story of this capture in "The Servicemen's Column":

In March of 1918, the *Yorktown* made a comic opera capture of a former Scripps research ship, the *Alexander Agassiz*, that was said to have been in Mazatlan outfitted as a German commerce raider . . . News reports made the tiny "Hun Raider" sound like a bristling battle ship.

Actually it carried a crew of five, including a woman, and didn't have a gun bigger than a rifle.

The *Yorktown* seized the 60-foot-long vessel off Mazatlan and brought it into San Diego. The prisoners were manacled and brought ashore under guard of sailors with fixed bayonets . . .

The Navy said the *Agassiz* was intended to capture American merchant ships, although it was never determined how this could be done with an armament of one or two rifles and a crew of five.

[15]Helen Raitt's interview with Mrs. W. C. Crandall in 1962. Even Dr. Ritter came under fire for alleged pro-German sympathies. When he was invited to address a community meeting on his views of the German war effort and dwelt, among other things, on German "efficiency," he met sharp criticism from the audience. The La Jolla *Journal* of August 3, 1917, began its report:

A violent attack from the trenches on the German position as outlined by Dr. Ritter converted last Monday night's Community House meeting into an open forum of a most rabid sort. One highly excited lady who objected to the speaker's alleged pro-German remarks was heard to mutter over and over again, "I can think of nothing but soft, ripe tomatoes."

CHAPTER IX

A NEW KIND OF INSTITUTION

[1]Ritter to President Wheeler, November 21, 1918.

[2]*Ibid.*

[3]Ritter to Crandall, April 15, 1921.

[4]Walter P. Taylor to Ritter, May 6, 1921. The significance of this information should not be underestimated. By 1917 Dr. Ritter, always interested in natural phenomena, had begun his study of the California woodpecker which led many years later to the publication of one of his most well-known books, *The California Woodpecker and I*. His humorous introduction to this book is explanatory: ". . . birds and men are much alike in doing essentially useful things to an absurdly useless degree. . ." (W. E. Ritter, *The California Woodpecker and I*, University of California Press, Berkeley, 1938, p. 4.)

[5]Crandall to Ritter, March 17, 1921.

[6]Crandall to Ellen B. Scripps, September 18, 1922.

[7]Crandall to Ellen B. Scripps, July 26, 1923.

[8]Ritter to W. A. Herdman, November 15, 1922.

[9]Ritter to Mary B. Ritter and staff, November 17, 1922.

[10]Crandall to J. W. Turrentine, March 8, 1923.

[11]F. B. Sumner, undated speech preserved in SIO Archives.

[12]Quoted by Mary B. Ritter in *More Than Gold in California, 1849-1933*, p. 368.

[13]F. B. Sumner, *Life History of an American Naturalist*, p. 208.

[14]F. B. Sumner, undated speech preserved in SIO Archives.

[15]W. B. France, "A Nature Hike on the Bottom of the Sea," San Diego *Sun*, July 16, 1925.

[16]Quoted by Mary B. Ritter in *More Than Gold in California*, 1849-1933, p. 364.

CHAPTER X
OCEANOGRAPHERS AGROUND

[1]T. Wayland Vaughan to President W. W. Campbell, March 18, 1927.

[2]North of the institution was grazing land and the Torrey Pines Reserve, which the city was able to make into a park with the help of Miss Scripps and Guy Fleming. In 1927 Fleming moved from the institution to his own home in the park near Torrey Pines Lodge. As naturalist, conservationist and superintendent of the state parks of the southern district, he carried out many park conservation projects such as the Anza-Borrego Desert State Park, Cuyamaca, Palomar and others.

[3]J. W. Gregg.

[4]The late Obie Maler, gardener who planted many of the eucalytus trees for Dr. Vaughan, took Helen Raitt on a tour of the campus on June 23, 1962. He pointed out where the eucalytus trees had survived on the south sides of canyons and at places where they were watered by leaks in the old wooden water pipe that crossed the institution's land. The eucalyptus trees planted as the border of the Biological Grade were six inches high when set out, he said, and these and other trees had to be watered by hand from a truck which carried tanks. Mr. Maler also described the city farm, sometimes called the Pueblo Farm, directly east of the institution, where many more eucalyptus trees were planted. This was run by the city and garbage was fed to the hogs kept there. Rude bunkhouses were maintained for itinerant workers who stopped by needing jobs.

[5]One of the most frequently recounted stories concerns the Vaughans' evening dinner parties, which were "rather formal" affairs served by a Filipino houseboy. As the finale on these occasions the houseboy would bring in three meatballs on a small silver plate, which he would present to Dr. Vaughan. The dignified director would then put his dog, invariably a German Shepherd, through a series of tricks to obtain these dainty rewards, and the meal would be brought to a close. Staff members during the Vaughan era never fail to mention Mrs. Dorothy Q. Vaughan, and feel that she was largely responsible for the "cultural tone" of the institution in these years. A niece of Oliver Wendell Holmes, Mrs. Vaughan had spent a large part of her girlhood in the Washington home of the Chief Justice, and was regarded as a lady of "real culture and refinement." She did much to further the institution's "town and gown" associations and was known as a gracious hostess to staff and visitors alike.

[6]Vaughan to Professor C. L. A. Schmidt, March 4, 1931.

[7]J. C. Harper to President W. W. Campbell, April 10, 1929.

[8]T. Wayland Vaughan, "Research Facilities at the Scripps Institution of Oceanography," The Collecting Net, Vol. viii, No. 1, July 1, 1933.

[9]Resolution adopted by the National Academy of Sciences on April 27, 1927, quoted in a memorandum from F. R. Lillie, Chairman of the Committee on Oceanography, to the members of the committee, June 15, 1927.

[10]In a letter dated May 26, 1927, Vaughan told Lillie that he had hoped different branches of oceanography would be represented. "At present," he noted, "the committee is composed of three biologists, one geologist and paleontologist, and myself a cross between a geologist and an oceanographer." The composition of the committee remained the same, however, although other scientists were brought in on some of the decision-making. In addition to Chairman F. R. Lillie, who was chairman of the Department of Zoology at the University of Chicago and (in 1928) president of the Marine Biological Laboratory at Woods Hole, Massachusetts, the members of the Committee on Oceanography were: William Bowie, Chief of the Division of Geodesy with the U. S. Coast and Geodetic Survey; E. G. Conklin, Professor of Zoology at Princeton University; B. M. Duggar, Professor of Plant Physiology at the University of Wisconsin and head of the Department of Botany at the Woods Hole Laboratory; John C. Merriam, President of the Carnegie Institution in Washington, D.C.; and T. Wayland Vaughan, Director of the Scripps Institution of Oceanography.

[11]F. R. Lillie to members of the Committee on Oceanography, June 15, 1927.

[12]A part of the Bigelow report, entitled *Oceanography, Its Scope, Problems and Economic Importance,* was subsequently published as a book.

[13]Woods Hole Oceanographic Institution was to be an entirely independent foundation, free from any governmental control, and an independent entity not dominated by some one university or group of universities.

[14]Vaughan to Lillie, November 29, 1929.

[15]W. E. Allen to President R. G. Sproul, July 25, 1929.

[16]Vaughan to J. C. Harper, February 26, 1934.

[17]O. B. Lokken to Vaughan, April 5, 1926.

[18]Vaughan to President R. G. Sproul, May 10, 1932.

CHAPTER XI

LOOKING SEAWARD

[1]Quoted in letter from Vaughan to Sproul, May 28, 1931.

[2]See appendix.

[3]Frank R. Lillie to Sproul, December 2, 1931.

[4]Vaughan to Sproul, May 10, 1932.

[5]*Ibid.*

[6]Vaughan to Louderback, December 28, 1935.

[7]Sverdrup had been offered other positions in the U.S. In a letter written on February 1, 1936, to Dean Vern O. Knudsen of the UCLA Graduate School, who had requested biographical information, he wrote: "I may add, confidentially, that I was again offered a position at the (Carnegie Institution) Department of Terrestrial Magnetism in 1930, and that if I had been ready to accept I would have been made the director of the Woods Hole Oceanographic Institution when that was organized in 1931."

[8]Vaughan to Louderback, December 28, 1935.

[9]Vaughan to Louderback, March 6, 1936.

[10]Memorandum from Bjorn Helland-Hansen dated November 18, 1935, preserved in SIO Archives.

[11]Helland-Hansen to Monroe F. Deutsch, November 16, 1935.

[12]Helland-Hansen to Vaughan, December 11, 1935.

[13]Louderback to Vaughan, December 19, 1935.

[14]H. U. Sverdrup to Vaughan, April 11, 1936.

[15]Dr. Sverdrup was accompanied by his attractive wife, Gudrun, and daughter Anna. After they were greeted at an outdoor supper at the Guy Flemings' Torrey Pines Park home the first evening, the Sverdrups soon moved into the Director's house vacated by the Vaughans. The dark redwood interiors were painted white in accordance with the Sverdrup's wishes, and the house took on a Scandinavian flavor.

[16]Sverdrup wrote a letter on January 15, 1937, to Captain Oakley J. Hall, manager of the Star & Crescent Boat Company which had acquired the *Scripps,* requesting a change of name. "I would consider it somewhat unfortunate and somewhat of a degradation if the name *SCRIPPS,* after having been applied to a research vessel, should be used for a garbage hauler," he noted. As a result the garbage scow ended its days with the more appropriate name of *Abraham Lincoln.*

[17]Graduate students of the year 1938-39, as stated in the annual report, included: C. C. Davis, Sallie May Davis, Peter Doudoroff, R. D. Gordon, John Lyman, C. R. Monk, Sydney Rittenberg, B. T. Scheer, Lois Sorkness and Richard Tibby.

[18]Nor had they foreseen its success. According to Miss Ruth Ragan, who typed the original manuscript and worked closely with the authors throughout, Sverdrup originally estimated that *The Oceans* might sell about 550 copies. Publishers Prentice-Hall report that to the end of 1965, 23,766 copies of the American edition have been sold and in foreign editions the work has had widespread sale abroad. Hailed from all sides as "the most comprehensive and authoritative" treatise yet published in the field, *The Oceans* contained 128 tables and 265 illustrations, many of which had been prepared by oceanographer Eugene C. La Fond.

CHAPTER XII

OCEANOGRAPHY AFLOAT

[1]Minutes of staff meeting September 22, 1936, preserved in SIO Archives.

[2]Annual Report, 1940.

[3]Sverdrup to President's office, November 8, 1939.

[4]Annual Report, 1941.

[5]*San Diego Sun*, January 15, 1939.

[6]These assistants were Kenneth Emery and Robert Dietz who were associated in various ways with the institution for some years.

[7]Microbiologist ZoBell joined the cruise at Guaymas. On the drive from La Jolla to that port, he was accompanied by Mrs. Revelle, Mrs. Shepard and Carl Johnson. This was the era when women were not allowed to step foot on the *E. W. Scripps*, and, according to their testimony, these two women were no exceptions.

[8]Sverdrup to Sproul, May 1, 1940.

CHAPTER XIII

WAR, WAVES AND REVERBERATIONS

[1]At the Radio and Sound Laboratory Revelle worked on problems of Radar Propagation and Harbor Defense and organized a Radar Operator's School, and in the latter part of the period was also officer in charge of the Sonar Division of the laboratory.

[2]The deep scattering layer was discovered by Henry Eyring, Ralph Christensen and Russell Raitt in studies being made to determine the causes of scattering of underwater sound which interfered with the detection of submarines by sonic echo ranging.

[3]Speech by H. U. Sverdrup: "Forecasting Sea, Swell and Surf for Amphibious Operations." Preserved in SIO Archives.

[4]Of the officers who studied at SIO in the war, a number of those who returned to Scripps Institution as graduate students are still involved in the field of oceanography. Robert Arthur, associated with SIO since 1944, is now a professor of oceanography. Wayne Burt is head of the department of Oceanography at Oregon State. Dale Leipper for a time directed the department at Texas A & M where Robert O. Reid joined him. Warren Thompson and Jacob Wickham have initiated the oceanographic program at the Navy's post graduate school in Monterey, California.

[5]Sverdrup's speech *op cit.*

[6]Dennis Fox was concerned with special investigations of the fouling of submerged surfaces for the U.S. Navy Bureau of Ships.

[7]To Scripps Institution of Oceanography, founded in 1912, and Woods Hole Oceanographic Institution, founded in 1930, had been added, after the war, Lamont Geological Observatory of Columbia University.

[8]Iselin to Sverdrup, April 10, 1946.

[9]F. N. D. Kurie to Sproul, February 8, 1946.

[10]Cochran to Sproul, January 3, 1946.

[11]The Office of Research and Inventions in Washington, D. C., was reorganized as the Office of Naval Research in 1945. Roger Revelle was made head of the Geophysics Branch of this office.

[12]Annual Report of Business Office, 1947.

[13]These temporary buildings, T1 and T2, still stand on the ocean front, south of the Director's office, in 1966. T3 came a short time later from Camp Elliot and provided a 1400 square foot machine shop. The building itself was obtained for $355, but cost $5000 to move and install.
Temporary buildings also housed graduate students of Scripps Institution after the war. This left-over war housing was located on the present site of Revelle College. Rents were minimal—$30.00 a month—and, according to reports, the buildings were substandard compared with the graduate student housing provided today.

[14]Biennial Report, 1946.

[15]*Popular Science*, November, 1949.

[16]Not all were in the best of condition. The *E. W. Scripps* had suffered from its wartime conversion and badly needed refitting. In December, 1948, the wife of the *Scripps* Captain became so concerned for her husband's safety aboard the ship that she had papers prepared, including marine surveyors reports and copies of letters from her husband, "sufficient to bring suit, against the University of California, the State of California, all responsible employees, in the amount of five hundred thousand dollars ($500,000) in the event the Motor Vessel *E. W. Scripps* is lost at sea." (SIO Archives.)
At a much later date the *E. W. Scripps* was retired and Roger Revelle told a reporter of its demise. "We sold it because the fastenings were all coming loose . . . Mike Todd bought it to use as the *Henrietta* in "Around the World in 80 Days." Then it became a South Seas island schooner. We heard not long ago that someone opened all the petcocks during a roaring party and now the *E. W. Scripps* rests at the bottom of Papeete Bay in Tahiti where all Oceanographers want to go when they die." Quote from Mary Hall, "Revelle" in *San Diego Magazine*, May, 1961, p. 133.

[17]Annual Report, Business Office, 1947.

[18]Sverdrup to James Corley, September 24, 1947.

[19]Quoted in Munk and Revelle's introduction to anniversary volume.

[20]*Ibid.*, p. 127.
Another interesting aspect of Sverdrup's experiences on the Maud expedition was his winter of 1920-21 among the Reindeer Chuckchi, one of the least known tribes of Eastern Siberia. He wrote a book on his attempt to live with these nomadic people who eat reindeer meat morning, noon and night, and told of their customs and how he learned their language. This amazing chronicle was published in Oslo in 1938 as *Hos Tundra-Folket*. While in La Jolla he attempted to publish his English translation "Reindeer Hair in My Food." His efforts did not meet with success and this translation reposes in the Scripps Institution of Oceanography's library today. Walter Munk remembers how Sverdrup entertained his students with stories of the Chuckchi tribe and demonstrated his physical fitness at the age of sixty by standing on his head.

[21]"Summary of Investigations—1950," manuscript prepared for *American Year Book*, 1950, preserved in SIO Archives.

[22]List of Scientific Personnel of Mid-Pacific Expedition

Horizon	EPCE (R) 857
Edward S. Barr	Jeremiah Black
George E. Brayton	William Batzler
Deane R. Carlson	Robert S. Dietz
Scott Cosby	Edwin Hamilton
Jeffery D. Frautschy	H. W. Menard
Louis E. Garrison	Joseph Roque
Daniel K. Gibson	Carl Shipek
Frank Hetzel	Lt. Com. D. J. McMillan
Robert P. Huffer	
John D. Isaacs	*University*
Martin W. Johnson	*of California Los Angeles*
Arthur E. Maxwell	James G. Edinger
Richard Y. Morita	David S. Johnson
Arthur D. Raff	Leon Sherman
Russell W. Raitt	
Roger R. Revelle	*University*
Thomas Runyan	*of Southern California*
James Snodgrass	Robert F. Dill
William Thompson	Kenneth O. Emery
Captain James Faughan	Sidney Rittenberg

[23]W. E. Ritter to W. A. Herdman, November 15, 1922.

[24]W. E. Ritter, *The Marine Biological Station*, 1912, p. 146-147.

[167]

APPENDICIES

APPENDIX A

First Membership List of the Marine Biological Association

24

San Diego. Cal. Sept. 26. 1903.

Pursuant to notice and call of the Committee on membership appointed at the last meeting the following persons met at the Chamber of Commerce rooms this evening. W. E. Ritter, E. W. Scripps. Miss Ellen Scripps, G. W. Fishburn. U. S. Grant, Col A. W. Voyclus. J. N. Newkirk. T. S. Brandegee, N. Cleveland. H. P. Wood M. L. Ward, Wm Clayton, F. S. Jennings. H. L. Titus R. C. Allen. J. B. Manning. Julius Wangenheim Geo. W. Marston, Ford A. Carpenter. C. Fred. Heilbron E. Stratlmann, Jas. MacMullen. Mrs. M. B. Coulston Geo. N. Hitchcock. Mr. & Mrs. Frank Stephens. F. W. Kelsey. W. J. Skilling. Dr. Annie Moore. C. J. Brown, F. R. Burnham P. C. Remondino. S. J. Black & Fred. Baker.

The meeting was called to order by the President Prof. W. E. Ritter. The minutes of the last meeting were read and approved. Prof. Ritter made a partial report on the work of the corps of biologists during the summer.

The reports of the membership committee and of the committee on organization were read together and were as follows:—

The following persons are recommended for membership and so far as they could be reached have been invited to attend this meeting:

Homer H. Peters, E. W. Scripps. F. J. Scripps, Miss Ellen Scripps. Miss Virginia Scripps. Mrs. Fannie Keating. Col. A. W. Voyde. M. S. Grant. & Geo. W. Marston, A. L. Spaulding, Julius Wangenheim, E. S. Babcock Graham Babcock J. W. Sefton. Ralph Granger. H. W. Putnam, F. S. Jennings. Wm Clayton, H. L. Titus. James MacMullen. J. N. Newkirk. Dr. F. R. Burnham. Dr. P. C. Remondino. Dr. J. A. Young. W. H Holcomb, Eugene Daney. Dr. Fred Baker F. W. Kelsey. Dr. Annie Moore Frank Stephens. Mrs. Frank Stephens. A. H. Frost. R. C. Allen. M. C. Healion. Ford A. Carpenter, F. S. Plimpton. G. W. Fishburn. C. Fred. Henking. D. C. Reed E. Strohlmann J. B. Mannix Mrs. Edward Snyder, W. J. Skilling. Dr. R. M. Powers. E. P. Ripley, J. D. Spreckels. Paul Morton.

The committee on organization reported a full set of by-laws as follows:—

1st. The undersigned hereby form themselves into an organization to be called the Marine Biological Association of San Diego, for the purpose

APPENDIX B

By-laws of the Marine Biological Association

1

By-Laws,
Of the San Diego. Marine Biological Association

I

The undersigned hereby form themselves into an organization to be called the Marine Biological Association of San Diego, for the purpose of securing the foundation and endowment of a scientific institution to be known as the San Diego Marine Biological Institution.

II

The general purposes of the institution shall be to carry on a biological and hydrographic survey of the waters of the Pacific Ocean adjacent to the coast of Southern California; to build and maintain a public aquarium and museum; and to prosecute such other kindred undertakings as the Board of Trustees may from time to time deem it wise to enter upon

III

The founding of the institution having

2

been perfected and its endowment secured, the whole or such part thereof as may in the judgement of the Trustees seem best, shall, under such conditions as the Trustees may impose, be transferred to the Regents of the University of California, to become a department of the University co-ordinate with its already existing departments

IV

The officers of the Association shall be a president, vice-president, scientific director secretary, and treasurer. In addition there shall be a Board of Trustees consisting of seven members, three of whom shall be the president, vice-president, and scientific director

V

The officers of the Association shall be elected at its first regular meeting and at each annual meeting of the Association thereafter, The annual meeting shall be held on the second Tuesday of July of each year. Should a quorum fail to be present at any annual meeting, a less number may adjourn from time to time until a quorum

APPENDIX C

La Jolla Calif apr. 21st 1915

Prof. C. A. Kofoid.

Dear Sir.

Yours of april 18th at hand.
Following is a list of La Jolla subscribers with amount
of subscription.

Chase & Ludington	$ 101.00
F. T. Scripp	100.00
Mr & Mrs J. L. Pearson.	30
Mrs Maxwell Smith.	25
Mr Charles S. Easton.	25
Mr Booker.	25
Mrs Mudgett.	15
Mr Walter Goforth.	15
Walter S Lieber	10
Mrs A. P. Mills.	10
Miss J Dudley	10
Mrs Carey	10
Mr Joseph Carey	10
Mrs Woodworth	10
Capt. Clark	10
Mr Devanney	10
Miss Sanders	5.00
Miss Coombs	5.00
	49.5

Name	Amount	Name	Amount
	45	W. W. Wetzel	370
Chas Toinni	$5	Mr J Brown	15
Mr H Fitzhugh	5	Mr Nicholson	10
Saml Kline	10	E O Elliot	5
Mrs Orr	2	Mrs M E Davis	5
W I Holston	5	E L Redding	5
Mrs Mary Mark	5	P Acton	5
Miss Hubbard	1	Mrs Keyes	5
Mrs H Ford Wells	10	Mr Barnes	20
A L Baily	25	Mr Rolfe	25
C. A. Bowker	5	Mrs Snyder	10
W. Genter	10	John Work	5
Dr J A Young	1.0	Mr E. H. Burr	5
J Wade McDonald	10	C. S. Dearborn	25
E. C. Thorp	25	Dr Woodward	10
Mrs C Murray	10	H. N. Lockwood	5
Rannalls & Son	5	Miss Ellen Mills	1
Upham & McCormack	5	Mr Swan	5
Miss Waddell	5	Emma F Chandler	5
Mary C Sharkey	5	Mrs Pebbles	10
Mrs McA Higley	15	Miss Jefferson	2
B Compton	5	Capt Griffen	5
T. J. Martin	5	Dr Oatman	10
J Holliday	10	George M Hawley	10
Mrs A Hodgson	5	Jos Flint	12
J. T. Rutherford	5	Jon Osborn	10
A P Smith	5	Mrs C C Derby	10
	633	(over)	878

APPENDIX D

Daniel Potter,

Notary Public in and for the County of

San Diego, State of California.

Recorded at Request of Nat. Bank, of Commerce, Aug. 20, 1907, at

15 min. past 10 o'clock, A.M.

John H. Ferry, County Recorder

By   Walter Forward, Deputy Recorder

Fee $1.20

STATE OF CALIFORNIA, } ss.
COUNTY OF SAN DIEGO

I, JOHN H. FERRY, County Recorder in and for San Diego County, State of California, do hereby
certify that I have compared the foregoing copy with the original record of a certain

Deed:

City of San Diego to Marine Biological Association

found and appearing of record in Book No. 423 of Deeds
at page 82 et seq., and that the same is a full, true and correct copy of such original record
and of the whole thereof.

IN WITNESS WHEREOF, I have hereunto set my hand and affixed my official Seal, this

19th day of February A. D. 190 9.

John H. Ferry, County Recorder.

By Geo. W. Moulton Deputy Recorder.

This Indenture made this 16th day of August, A.D. 1907, between the City of San Diego, a municipal corporation of the County of San Diego, State of California, the party of the first part, and the Marine Biological Association, of the San Diego, a corporation, duly organized and existing under the laws of the State of California, the party of the second part, Witnesseth:

Whereas, on the 10th day of August, 1907, pursuant to published notice of sale, the said party of the first part did offer for sale, to the highest bidder at public auction, all the right, title and interest of the said City in and to certain lands hereinafter described, and

Whereas at such sale the party of the second part bid the sum of One Thousand (1000.00) Dollars for said land, and

Whereas said amount was the highest bid received by said party of the first part for said land, and said party of the second part was the highest bidder therefor and said land was thereupon sold to said party of the second part, and

Whereas the Common Council of said City of San Diego, duly adopted Ordinance No. 3000 on the 12th day of August, 1907, ratifying and confirming said sale, which said Ordinance was approved by the Mayor of said City on the 14th day of August, 1907, and

Whereas in said Ordinance the Mayor and the Clerk of said City were authorized and directed to execute a deed to said land to said party of the second part, conveying all the right, title and interest of said party of the first part thereto.

Now, Therefore, the said party of the first part in consideration of the sum of One Thousand (1,000.00) Dollars, lawful money of the United States of America, to it in hand paid by the said party of the second part the receipt whereof is hereby acknowledged, does by these presents sell, remise, release quitclaim and convey unto the said party of the second part, its successors and assigns, forever, all the right, title and interest of the said party of the first part in and to the following tract or parcel of land lying in the City of San Diego, County of San Diego, State of California, and particularly described as follows, to-wit:

Pueblo Lot number Twelve Hundred Ninety-eight (1298) of the Pueblo Lands of the said City of San Diego, according to the official map of said Pueblo Lands as made by James Pascoe now on file in the office of the Recorder of the said County of San Diego, excepting and reserving therefrom a strip of land one hundred (100) feet wide through said Pueblo Lot Number Twelve Hundred Ninety-eight (1298) as a right of way for the Boulevard extending from La Jolla Park to the Torrey Pines in said City.

To Have and to Hold the above quitclaimed premises unto the said party of the second part its successors and assigns forever.

In Witness Whereof, the said party of the first part has caused these presents to be executed in its corporate name by its Mayor and attested by its Clerk and its corporate seal to be hereunto attached the day and year first above written.

The	City of San Diego, California.
City of	By Jno. F. Forward,
San Diego,	Mayor of the City of San Diego, California.
State of	Attest: J. T. Butler,
California.	Clerk of the City of San Diego.

State of California, ⎫ ss.
County of San Diego. ⎬

On this 16th day of August, in the year A.D. 1907, before me, Daniel Potter, a Notary Public in and for said County, residing therein, duly commissioned and sworn, personally appeared John F. Forward, and J. T. Butler, personally known to me to be the Mayor and Clerk, respectively, of the corporation that executed the foregoing instrument, and acknowledged to me that such corporation executed the same.

In Witness Whereof, I have hereunto set my hand and affixed my official seal at my office, in the City of San Diego, County of San Diego, State of California, the day and year in this certificate first above written.

APPENDIX E
(Copy)

Mar 31/14

In pursuance of the authority and direction granted and given by item "C" of its enumerated powers as set forth in its articles of incorporation; and by a resolution regularly adopted as a special meeting of its members, duly and regularly called, and held on the 23rd day of February, 1912; and by an order of the Superior Court of the County of San Diego, State of California, duly and regularly made on the 8th day of March 1912.

MARINE BIOLOGICAL ASSOCIATION OF SAN DIEGO, a corporation duly organized and existing under the laws of the State of California, for and in consideration of the sum of Ten Dollars ($10.00) and other valuable considerations, does hereby grant to The Regents of the University of California, the same to become a department of the State University, co-ordinate with the already existing departments and to be used exclusively for the purpose of maintaining, improving and developing The Scripps Institution for Biological Research of the University of California, with power to sell, lease, rent, improve or otherwise dispose of and manage the same, or any part thereof, and apply the proceeds and rentals to such purposes, the following described real property situated in the City of San Diego, County of San Diego, State of California, to-wit:

Pueblo Lot numbered twelve hundred ninety-eight (1298) of the Pueblo lands of the said City of San Diego, according to the official map of said Pueblo Lands as made by James Pascoe, now on file in the office of the Recorder of said County of San Diego, excepting and reserving therefrom a strip of land one hundred (100) feet wide through said Pueblo Lot Twelve hundred ninety-eight (1298) as right of way for the Boulevard extending from La Jolla Park to the Torrey Pines in said City.

TO HAVE AND TO HOLD the above granted and described premises unto the said Grantee, its heirs and assigns forever.

This deed is executed to evidence the transfer of the said lands by said Marine Biological Association of San Diego to The Regents of the University of California by deed dated March 13, 1913, which last mentioned deed was lost after being delivered to the grantee therein named, and before being placed of record.

IN WITNESS WHEREOF, the said corporation has caused its President and Secretary to execute this instrument and affix the corporate seal hereto this 31st day of March, 1914.

x x x x x x x x   MARINE BIOLOGICAL ASSOCIATION
x   x   OF SAN DIEGO.
x Corporate x
x   Seal   x   By (signed) Fred Baker, President.
x   x
x x x x x x x x   By (signed) W. C. Crandall, Secretary.

STATE OF CALIFORNIA, ⎱ SS.
County of San Diego.   ⎰

On this 31st day of March, 1914, before me, Edwin Reed, a Notary Public in and for the County of San Diego, State of California, duly commissioned and sworn, and residing therein, personally appeared W. C. Crandall, known to me to be the Secretary of the corporation that executed the within instrument, and acknowledged to me that such corporation executed the same.

Berkeley, February 14, 1912.

My dear Professor Ritter:

Enclosed is a copy of the report of the
Special Committee on the Scripps matter. The report
was duly approved by the Board at their meeting of
February 13, and President Wheeler and Mr. Earl at
once signed the letter and delivered it to Mr. Schoonover.
My heartiest congratulations on the excellent outcome!

Very sincerely yours,

Professor W E. Ritter,
    La Jolla,
        California.

Enclosure.

REPORT OF SPECIAL COMMITTEE

SAN FRANCISCO, February 13, 1912.

To the Honorable Board of Regents:

Your Special Committee has the honor of reporting that a conference was held at San Diego between representatives of the San Diego Marine Biological Association, representatives of Miss Ellen B. Scripps, and of Mr. E. W. Scripps, Professor William E. Ritter (Director of the San Diego Marine Biological Laboratory), President Wheeler, Regent McKinley, and Regent Earl. The result of this conference was full agreement as to the desirability of the transfer to the Regents at this time of the property of the Marine Biological Association of San Diego. We have the honor of recommending that the President of the University and the Chairman of the Finance Committee be authorized to address the following letter to the officers and members of the Marine Biological Association of San Diego:

"BERKELEY, CALIFORNIA, February 13, 1912.

"To the Officers and Members of the Marine Biological Association of San Diego, San Diego, California:

"In contemplation of the transfer by your association of the whole of its properties, rights, and privileges to the Regents of the University of California we would say: As we stated to representatives of your association at a meeting held in San Diego a few days ago, the Regents of the University of California and the officers of the University appreciate fully the importance of the work being done at the Marine Biological Station at San Diego and of the great value, present and prospective, of the properties acquired and held by your association in connection therewith.

"The Regents and the officers of the University recognize also that the development of the station to its present efficiency, and the acquisition by your association of its properties, is largely due to the work of Professor William E. Ritter and his colleagues, aided and encouraged by the financial support of Miss Ellen B. Scripps and Mr. E. W. Scripps. The Regents and the officers of the University are advised, also, that Miss Ellen B. Scripps would be pleased to have her liberal donations to the station, and its development, serve as a memorial to her deceased brother, George H. Scripps.

"In the event that a transfer of the property is made by your association to the Regents of the University of California, it will be accepted by the Regents of the University of California in trust for the following purposes:

"1. To become a department of the University, coördinate with its already existing departments; and to have a like status and recognition to that now accorded to the Lick Observatory.

"2. During the lifetime of Miss Ellen B. Scripps and until the final settlement of her estate the management and control of the affairs of the station and properties shall be in the hands of a local board at San Diego, consisting of Miss Ellen B. Scripps, President Benjamin Ide Wheeler, E. W. Scripps, and Wm. E. Ritter, and such other persons as may be mutually agreed upon by them, with authority to name an executive committee of three members; that during such period the sum of one thousand dollars per annum will be paid by the University to Professor William E. Ritter as heretofore.

"3. That during the lifetime of Miss Ellen B. Scripps, and while the affairs of the station are under the control of such local board, and thereafter, the Regents and the officers of the University will use their best efforts to secure the largest possible state appropriations to promote the work of the station.

"4. Whenever funds of the University are available for the purpose the same will be devoted to the work and development of the station.

"5. The official designation of the Station shall be 'The Scripps Institution for Biological Research, of the University of California.'

"6. The station, and the properties of your association, will be accepted by the Regents of the University of California in trust for the purpose of making it, as a part of the University of California, an instrument for the most liberal biological research and the free expression and publication of the results of such research, as intended by its founders.

"President.

"Chairman of the Finance Committee."

Respectfully submitted,

Special Committee.

[182]

APPENDIX F

History of the Administration of SIO

September	1903-September	1923	William E. Ritter—*Director*
September	1923-February	1924	Francis B. Sumner—*Acting Director*
February	1924-August	1936	T. Wayland Vaughan—*Director*
September	1936-February	1948	Harald U. Sverdrup—*Director*
March	1948-February	1950	Carl Eckart—*Director*
March	1950-July	1951	Robert R. Revelle—*Acting Director*
July	1951-September	1961	Roger R. Revelle—*Director*
October	1961-June	1963	Roger R. Revelle—*Director on leave* Fred N. Spiess—*Acting Director*
July	1963-September	1964	Roger R. Revelle—*Director*
October	1964-June	1965	Fred N. Spiess—*Director*
July	1965-		William A. Nierenberg—*Director* Fred N. Spiess—*Associate Director* Andrew A. Benson—*Associate Director*

APPENDIX G

The Scripps Institution of Oceanography
Officers of the Institution

1912

RESIDENT STAFF

Wm. E. Ritter, Ph.D., Director.

E. L. Michael, M.S., Zoologist and Administrative Assistant.

G. F. McEwen, Ph.D., Hydrographer.

NON-RESIDENT STAFF

C. A. Kofoid, Ph.D., Assistant Director, Professor of Zoology, University of California.

C. O. Esterly, Ph.D., Zoologist, Professor of Zoology, Occidental College, Los Angeles, California.

W. C. Crandall, A.B., Master of the *Alexander Agassiz*, Professor of Biology, State Normal School, San Diego.

Myrtle E. Johnson, Ph.D., Zoologist, Teacher of Biology, Pasadena High School, Pasadena, California.

H. C. Burbridge, A.B., Chemist, Assistant in Physics, Leland Stanford Junior University.

J. Frank Daniel, Ph.D., Special Investigator on Elasmobranch Fishes, Assistant Professor of Zoology, University of California.

A. L. Barrows, M.S., Assistant in Zoology, University of California.

[183]

OFFICERS OF THE INSTITUTION

BENJ. IDE WHEELER, Ph.D., LL.D., Litt.D., L.H.D., President of the University, Berkeley.

RESIDENT OFFICERS

WILLIAM E. RITTER, Ph.D., Scientific Director and Professor of Zoology.

W. C. CRANDALL, A.B., Business Agent.

F. B. SUMNER, Ph.D., Biologist.

E. L. MICHAEL, M.S., Zoologist and Administrative Assistant.

GEORGE F. McEWEN, Ph.D., Hydrographer and Curator of the Oceanographic Museum.

CHRISTINE E. ESSENBERG, Ph.D., Zoologist and Librarian.

P. S. BARNHART, M.S., Curator of Aquarium and Collector.

R. P. BRANDT, Ph.D., Botanist, for Special Investigation on Kelp.

H. H. COLLINS, M.S., Research Assistant.

NON-RESIDENT OFFICERS

C. A. KOFOID, Ph.D., Sc.D., Zoologist and Assistant Director, Professor of Zoology, University of California, Berkeley.

C. O. ESTERLY, Ph.D., Zoologist, Professor of Zoology, Occidental College, Los Angeles, California.

J. FRANK DANIEL, Ph.D., Special Investigator on Elasmobranch Fishes, Associate Professor of Zoology, University of California, Berkeley.

1926-1927

OFFICERS OF THE INSTITUTION

WILLIAM WALLACE CAMPBELL, Sc.D., LLD., President of the University.

WILLIAM E. RITTER, Ph.D., Professor of Zoology, Emeritus.

RESIDENT OFFICERS

T. WAYLAND VAUGHAN, Ph.D., Director and Professor of Oceanography.

F. B. SUMNER, Ph.D., Professor of Biology.

GEORGE F. McEWEN, Ph.D., Associate Professor, Physical Oceanographer and Curator of Physical Oceanography.

W. E. ALLEN, M.A., Assistant Professor of Biology.

E. G. MOBERG, Ph.D., Instructor in Chemical Oceanography.

P. S. BARNHART, M.S., Associate in Oceanography and Curator of Biological Collection.

S. W. Chambers, Assistant in Physical Oceanography.
James Ross, Captain of boat "Scripps" and Superintendent of Grounds and Buildings.
Tillie Genter, Secretary and Librarian.

NON-RESIDENT OFFICER

*C. O. Esterley, Ph.D., Zoologist; Professor of Zoology, Occidental College, Los Angeles, California.

1934-1935

OFFICERS OF THE INSTITUTION

Robert Gordon Sproul, B.S., LL.D., President of the University.
William Wallace Campbell, Sc.D., LL.D., President of the University, Emeritus.
William E. Ritter, Ph.D., LL.D., Professor of Zoology, Emeritus.

RESIDENT OFFICERS

T. Wayland Vaughan, Ph.D., LL.D., Director, and Professor of Oceanography.
F. B. Sumner, Ph.D., Professor of Biology.
George F. McEwen, Ph.D., Professor, Physical Oceanographer, and Curator of Physical Oceanography.
W. E. Allen, M.A., Assistant Professor of Biology.
E. G. Moberg, Ph.D., Assistant Professor of Oceanography, and in charge of the boat "Scripps."
D. L. Fox, Ph.D., Instructor in Physiology of Marine Organisms.
M. W. Johnson, Ph.D., Instructor in Marine Biology.
C. E. ZoBell, Ph.D., Instructor in Marine Microbiology.
P. S. Barnhart, M.S., Associate in Oceanography and Curator of Biological Collection.
S. W. Chambers, Associate in Physical Oceanography.
Fred Baker, M.D., Honorary Curator of Mollusks.
Easter E. Cupp, Ph.D., Research Associate in Oceanography.
R. H. Fleming, Ph.D., Research Associate in Oceanography.
Peter Doudoroff, A.B., Research Assistant in Oceanography.
R. R. Revelle, A.B., Research Assistant in Oceanography.
D. Q. Anderson, M.S., Technical Assistant.
Ursel S. Armstrong, A.B., Technical Assistant.
Katherine Gehring, Technical Assistant.
E. C. La Fond, A.B., Technical Assistant.

[185]

MARK SHEFFIELD, General Assistant.

JAMES ROSS, Superintendent of Grounds and Buildings.

M. G. ROSS, Engineer of boat "Scripps."

TILLIE GENTER, Secretary.

RUTH RAGAN, A.B., Assistant Secretary.

RUTH McKITRICK, Stenographer.

1948

OFFICERS OF THE INSTITUTION

HARALD U. SVERDRUP, Ph.D., Professor of Oceanography and Director of the Scripps Institution of Oceanography.

CARL L. HUBBS, Ph.D., Professor of Biology.

GEORGE F. McEWEN, Ph.D., Professor of Physical Oceanography and Curator of Physical Oceanography.

NORRIS W. RAKESTRAW, Ph.D., Professor of Chemistry.

T. WAYLAND VAUGHAN, Ph.D., Professor of Oceanography and Director, Emeritus.

DENIS L. FOX, Ph.D., Associate Professor of Marine Biochemistry.

MARTIN W. JOHNSON, Ph.D., Associate Professor of Marine Biology.

ROGER R. REVELLE, Ph.D., Associate Professor of Oceanography.

CLAUDE E. ZOBELL, Ph.D., Associate Professor of Marine Microbiology and Assistant to the Director.

WINFRED E. ALLEN, M.A., Assistant Professor of Biology, Emeritus.

WALTER H. MUNK, Ph.D., Assistant Professor of Geophysics.

MARSTON C. SARGENT, Ph.D., Assistant Professor of Oceanography.

DAYTON E. CARRITT, Instructor.

THEODORE J. WALKER, Instructor.

PERCY S. BARNHART, M.S., Associate in Oceanography and Curator of Biological Collection, Emeritus.

SAM D. HINTON, Curator of Museum.

STANLEY W. CHAMBERS, Associate in Physical Oceanography.

FRANCIS P. SHEPARD, Ph.D., Associate in Marine Geology.

EARLE D. HAMMOND, Captain "E. W. Scripps."

SHELDON C. CRANE, Research Assistant.

WILLIAM E. HUTTON, Research Assistant.

J. BENNET OLSON, Research Assistant.

FREDERICK D. SISLER, Research Assistant.

WARREN W. WOOSTER, Research Assistant.

CLAUDE W. PALMER, Senior Laboratory Assistant.

PAUL WILLIAMS, Senior Laboratory Assistant.
CARL I. JOHNSON, Buildings and Grounds Foreman.
TILLIE GENTER, Secretary.
HARRIET DUNN, Secretary.
RUTH RAGAN, A.B., Librarian 2.
KATHERINE ATWOOD, Senior Library Assistant.
GOLDIE B. FLOYD, Statistical Clerk.
JEAN E .SULLIVAN, Laboratory Technician.
CLARA HILL, Typist-Clerk.
LEONA PHIPPS, Telephone Operator.

1950

OFFICERS OF THE INSTITUTION

CARL ECKART, Ph.D., Professor of Geophysics and Acting Director of the Scripps Institution of Oceanography.

DENIS L. FOX, Ph.D., Professor of Marine Biochemistry.

CARL L. HUBBS, Ph.D., Professor of Biology.

MARTIN W. JOHNSON, Ph.D., Professor of Marine Biology.

GEORGE F. MCEWEN, Ph.D., Professor of Physical Oceanography and Curator of Physical Oceanography.

NORRIS W. RAKESTRAW, Ph.D., Professor of Chemistry.

ROGER REVELLE, Ph.D., Professor of Oceanography and Associate Director of the Scripps Institution of Oceanography.

FRANCIS P. SHEPARD, Ph.D., Professor of Submarine Geology.

HARALD U. SVERDRUP, Ph.D., Professor of Oceanography and Director, Emeritus.

T. WAYLAND VAUGHAN, Ph.D., Professor of Oceanography and Director, Emeritus.

CLAUDE E. ZOBELL, Ph.D., Professor of Marine Microbiology.

LEONARD N. LIEBERMANN, Ph.D., Associate Professor of Geophysics.

WALTER H. MUNK, Ph.D., Associate Professor of Geophysics.

RUSSELL W. RAITT, Ph.D., Associate Professor of Geophysics.

MARSTON C. SARGENT, Ph.D., Assistant Professor of Oceanography.

THEODORE J. WALKER, Ph.D., Instructor in Oceanography.

FRED B. PHLEGER, Ph.D., Visiting Associate Professor of Submarine Geology.

ROBERT S. DEITZ, Ph.D., Lecturer in Submarine Geology.

R. DANA RUSSELL, Ph.D., Lecturer in Submarine Geology.

JOHN D. ISAACS, B.S., Associate Oceanographer.

JAMES M. SNODGRASS, A.B., Associate Marine Biologist.

EDWARD D. GOLDBERG, Ph.D., Assistant Marine Chemist.

JOHN L. McHUGH, M.A., Assistant Marine Biologist.

ROBERT O. REID, M.S., Assistant Oceanographer.

PHILIP RUDNICK, Ph.D., Assistant Physicist.

VICTOR C. ANDERSON, B.S., Research Associate.

DANIEL E. ANDREWS, B.S., Research Associate.

STANLEY W. CHAMBERS, A.B., Research Associate.

WESLEY R. COE, Ph.D., Sc.D., Research Associate.

FREDERICK D. SISLER, Ph.D., Research Associate.

BEATRICE M. SWEENEY, Ph.D., Research Associate.

JOHN D. COCHRANE, M.S., Associate in Oceanography.

GIFFORD C. EWING, M.S., Associate in Oceanography.

JEFFERY D. FRAUTSCHY, B.S., Associate in Marine Geology.

PAUL L. HORRER, M.S., Associate in Oceanography.

DOUGLAS L. INMAN, M.S., Associate in Marine Geology.

PALMER OSBORN, M.S., Associate in Oceanography.

JAMES RUSK, M.S., Associate in Oceanography.

WARREN B. WOOSTER, M.S., Associate in Oceanography.

WILLIAM G. VAN DORN, M.S., Associate in Oceanography.

THOMAS E. BOWMAN, M.S., Assistant in Marine Biology.

THEODORE R. FOLSOM, M.S., Assistant in Oceanography.

LOUIS W. KIDD, B.S., Assistant in Oceanography.

WILLIAM L. SPIX, B.S., Assistant in Marine Chemistry.

JAMES L. FAUGHN, B.S., Marine Superintendent, Engineering.

DOROTHEA FOX, A.B., Acting Librarian.

SAM D. HINTON, A.B., Senior Museum Zoologist.

JOHN C. KIRBY, Senior Administrative Assistant.

FINN W. OUTLER, Marine Technical Superintendent.

FRANCES E. SPARKS, Secretary.

CLEMENS W. STOSE, Marine Superintendent, Hull.

DON D. WILKERSON, Grounds and Buildings, Superintendent.

MELVIN WATTENBERG, B.S., Accountant.

1966

JOHN S. GALBRAITH, Chancellor of U.C.S.D.

WILLIAM A. NIERENBERG, Director of Scripps Institution of Oceanography.

Fred N. Spiess, Associate Director of Scripps Institution of Oceanography and Director of Marine Physical Laboratory.

Andrew A. Benson, Associate Director of Scripps Institution of Oceanography and Chairman of the Marine Biology Division.

Jeffery D. Frautschy, Assistant Director of Scripps Institution of Oceanography.

Carl Eckart, Vice Chancellor of U.C.S.D. and member of Scripps Institution Staff Council.

Walter H. Munk, Associate Director of Institute of Geophysics and Planetary Physics.

Milner B. Schaefer, Director of Institute of Marine Resources.

OCEANIC RESEARCH DIVISION

Robert S. Arthur
George S. Bien
Brian P. Boden
Douglas R. Caldwell
Tsaihwa J. Chow
Charles S. Cox
Joseph R. Curray
James T. Enright
E. W. Fager
Robert L. Fisher
Arthur O. Flechsig
Theodore R. Folsom
Myrl C. Hendershott
Douglas L. Inman
Charles D. Keeling
Ferren MacIntyre
John A. McGowan
M. S. Longuet Higgins (one quarter)

James R. Moriarty
Michael M. Mullin
William A. Newman
Frances L. Parker
Melvin N. A. Peterson
Fred B Phleger
William R. Riedel
Margaret K. Robinson
Andre M. Rosfelder
Francis P. Shepard
George G. Shor, Jr. (Chairman)
Bruce A. Taft
Tjeerd H. van Andel
William G. Van Dorn
Theodore J. Walker
Edward L. Winterer
Warren S. Wooster

EARTH SCIENCE DIVISION

Gustaf O. S. Arrhenius
George C. Backus
Manuel N. Bass
Rudolf Bieri
E. C. Bullard (one quarter)
Thomas E. Chase
Harmon Craig (Chairman)
Albert E. J. Engel
Jane Z. Frazer
J. Freeman Gilbert

Edward D. Goldberg
John J. Griffin
Richard Haubrich
Minoru Koide
Henry W. Menard
Walter H. Munk
Russell W. Raitt
Archibald M. Reid
Stuart M. Smith
Victor Vacquier

MARINE BIOLOGY DIVISION

ANDREW A. BENSON (Chairman)
ELIZABETH K. BODEN
DENIS L. FOX
SUSUMU HAGIWARA
FRANCIS T. HAXO
NICHOLAS D. HOLLAND
CARL L. HUBBS
REUBEN LASKER

RALPH A. LEWIN
BERNHARD E. REIMANN
RICHARD H. ROSENBLATT
PER F. SCHOLANDER
BENJAMIN E. VOLCANI
ROBERT L. WISNER
CLAUDE E. ZOBELL

MARINE PHYSICAL LABORATORY

VICTOR C. ANDERSON
(Associate Director)
FREDERICK H. FISHER
LEONARD N. LIEBERMANN
CARL D. LOWENSTEIN
JOHN MUDIE
JOHN NORTHROP
BENTON B. OWEN

ARTHUR RAFF
RUSSELL W. RAITT
ROBERT A. RASMUSSEN
PHILIP RUDNICK
GEORGE C. SHOR, JR.
FRED N. SPIESS (Director)
VICTOR VACQUIER

VISIBILITY LABORATORY

ROSWELL W. AUSTIN
ALMERIAN R. BOILEAU
SEIBERT Q. DUNTLEY (Director)
JAMES L. HARRIS

RUDOLPH W. PREISENDORFER
RAYMOND C. SMITH
JOHN H. TAYLOR
JOHN E. TYLER

INSTITUTION OF GEOPHYSICS AND PLANETARY PHYSICS

GEORGE E. BACKUS
BARRY BLOCK
HUGH BRADNER
DOUGLAS R. CALDWELL
J. FREEMAN GILBERT

RICHARD A. HAUBRICH
CARL E. McILVAINE
JOHN W. MILES
WALTER MUNK (Director)
FRANK E. SNODGRASS

INSTITUTE OF MARINE RESOURCES

JOHN R. BEERS
MAURICE BLACKBURN
R. W. EPPLEY
ROBERT D. HAMILTON
ROBERT W. HOLMES
OSMUND HOLM-HANSEN
ALAN R. LONGHURST

CARL LORENZEN
MICHAEL M. MULLIN
MILNER B. SCHAEFER (Director)
JOHN D. STRICKLAND
WILLIAM H. THOMAS
P. M. WILLIAMS

MARINE LIFE RESEARCH GROUP

ANGELES ALVARINO DE LEIRA
EDWARD BRINTON (on leave)

ABRAHAM FLEMINGER
JOHN D. ISAACS (Director)

Martin W. Johnson
Hans T. Klein
Margaret Knight
John A. McGowan
Julian K. Miller

Joseph L. Reid, Jr.
Walter R. Schmitt
Richard A. Schwartzlose
Angelo F. Carlucci

APPLIED OCEANOGRAPHY GROUP
Edward D. McAlister (Director)   William L. McLeish

PHYSIOLOGICAL RESEARCH LABORATORY
Robert W. Elsner
Theodore Enns
Dean L. Franklin

Susumu Hagiwara (Associate Director)
Edward Hemmingsen
Per F. Scholander (Director)

SALT WATER TEST FACILITY
Leroy A. Bromley

EMERITUS
Milton N. Bramlette
Carl Hubbs
Martin W. Johnson
Norris Rakestraw

Roger R. Revelle
George F. McEwen
Francis P. Shepard
Charles D. Wheelock

ADDITIONAL MEMBERS OF SCRIPPS INSTITUTION STAFF COUNCIL
Nelson Fuller, Publications and Public Information, SIO
Joseph Gantner, Librarian
Marston Sargent, Scientific Liaison Officer for the Office of Naval Research, Scripps Institution of Oceanography
Maxwell Silverman, Marine Engineer
James M. Snodgrass, Special Developments
James Stewart, Diving Officer
Peter Trapani, Marine Facilities
Donald W. Wilkie, Curator, Thomas Wayland Vaughan Aquarium-Museum

ASSOCIATED GROUPS ON SCRIPPS CAMPUS AT BUREAU OF COMMERCIAL FISHERIES
Elbert Ahlstrom, Director, California Current Resources, U. S. Bureau of Commercial Fisheries
Gerald Howard, Director of Tuna Resources Laboratory, U. S. Bureau of Commercial Fisheries
John Kask, Director, Inter-American Tropical Tuna Commission

RESEARCH ASSOCIATES

Elbert H. Ahlstrom
John L. Baxter
E. Grey Dimond
John E. Fitch
Kurt Fredriksson
Edwin L. Hamilton
Gerald V. Howard
David Jensen
John L. Kask

Pedro Mercado-Sanchez
Garth I. Murphy
Richard P. Phillips
J. Radovich
Guillermo P. Salas
Marston C. Sargent
Charles R. Schroeder
Thomas Whitaker
Richard R. Whitney

APPENDIX H

Ph.D. Degrees were granted to these candidates who did the bulk of their work or all at Scripps Institution of Oceanography, University of California, 1912-1966

DATE	NAME	FIELD	WHERE CONFERRED
1919	Henry Homer Collins	Zoology	UC, Berkeley
1924	Ralph Ruskin Huestis	Zoology	UC, Berkeley
1925	Erik Gustaf Moberg	Biochemistry	UC, Berkeley
1930	Ancel Benjamin Keys	Biological Oceanography	UC, Berkeley
1934	Easter Ellen Cupp	Biological Oceanography	UC, Berkeley
	Earl Hamlet Myers	Biological Oceanography	UC, Berkeley
	Eldon Marion Thorp	Geological Oceanography	UC, Berkeley
	Nelson Alfred Wells	Biological Oceanography	UC, Berkeley
1935	Richard Howell Fleming	Oceanography	UC, Berkeley
1936	Roger Randall Revelle	Oceanography	UC, Berkeley
1940	Bradley Titus Scheer	Comparative Physiology	UC, Berkeley
	Charles Carroll Davis	Zoology	U. of Washington
1941	Peter Doudoroff	Zoology	UC, Berkeley
	Sydney Charles Rittenberg	Microbiology	UC, Berkeley
1942	Cecil Ray Monk	Zoology	UCLA
1943	James Clark Hindman	Oceanography	UCLA
1944	Richard Bitner Tibby	Oceanography	UCLA
1945	William David Rosenfeld	Microbiology	UCLA
1946	Josephine Beckwith Senn	Microbiology	UCLA
1947	Walter Heinrich Munk	Oceanography	UCLA
1948	Woodrow Cooper Jacobs	Oceanography	UCLA
	David Maule Updegraff	Microbiology	UCLA

DATE	NAME	FIELD	WHERE CONFERRED
1949	SHELDON CYR CRANE	Physical-Biological Science	UCLA
	WILLIAM ELMER HUTTON	Microbiology	UCLA
	FREDERICK DAVID SISLER	Microbiology	UCLA
	BOYD WALLACE WALKER	Zoology	UCLA
	GEORGE FERDINAND WEISEL, JR.	Zoology	UCLA
1950	ROBERT SIPLE ARTHUR	Oceanography	UCLA
	BRIAN PETER BODEN	Oceanography	UCLA
	ELIZABETH MAITLAND KAMPA	Zoology	UCLA
	JOHN LAURENCE MCHUGH	Zoology	UCLA
	JOHN BENNET OLSON	Zoology	UCLA
1951	WILLIAM SHERMAN BUTCHER	Oceanography	UCLA
	WILLIAM MAXWELL CAMERON	Oceanography	UCLA
	GIFFORD COCHRAN EWING	Oceanography	UCLA
	DALE FREDERICK LEIPPER	Oceanography	UCLA
	JOHN CALVIN LUDWICK, JR.	Oceanography	UCLA
	ROBERT MATHESON NORRIS	Oceanography	UCLA
	CARL HENRY OPPENHEIMER	Microbiology	UCLA
1952	WAYNE VINCENT BURT	Oceanography	UCLA
	THEODORE ROBERT FOLSOM	Oceanography	UCLA
	HAN-LEE MAO	Oceanography	UCLA
	DONALD WILLIAM PRITCHARD	Oceanography	UCLA
1953	ERNEST ROBERT ANDERSON	Oceanography	UCLA
	VICTOR CHARLES ANDERSON	Physics	UCLA
	ALFRED JAMES CARSOLA	Oceanography	UCLA
	DOUGLAS LAMAR INMAN	Oceanography	UCLA
	WHEELER JAMES NORTH	Oceanography	UCLA
	PHILIP CHALLACOMBE SCRUTON	Oceanography	UCLA
	WARREN SCRIVER WOOSTER	Oceanography	UCLA
1954	THOMAS ELLIOT BOWMAN	Zoology	UCLA
	WILLIAM GEORGE VAN DORN	Oceanography	UCLA
	WILLIAM RALPH WALTON	Oceanography	UCLA
1955	CHARLES SHIPLEY COX	Oceanography	UCLA
	RICHARD YUKIO MORITA	Microbiology	UCLA
	NORIYUKI NASU	Oceanography	UCLA
	COLM OH EOCHA	Oceanography	UCLA
1956	SAYED ALY EL WARDINI	Oceanography	UCLA
	EARL EVERETT GOSSARD	Oceanography	UCLA
	GORDON WILLIAM GROVES	Oceanography	UCLA
	ALAN STEWART HOURSTON	Oceanography	UCLA
	RUDOLPH WILLIAM PREISENDORFER	Mathematics	UCLA
	ANDREAS BUCHWALD RECHNITZER	Zoology	UCLA

DATE	NAME	FIELD	WHERE CONFERRED
	Harris Bates Stewart, Jr.	Oceanography	UCLA
1957	David Kilgore Arthur	Oceanography	UCLA
	Leo De Witte Berner, Jr.	Oceanography	UCLA
	Frederick Hendrick Fisher	Physics	U. of Washington
	Robert Lloyd Fisher	Oceanography	UCLA
	Hugh John McLellan	Oceanography	UCLA
	June Grace Pattullo	Oceanography	UCLA
	Adrian Frank Richards	Oceanography	UCLA
	Frederick Henry Carlyle Taylor	Oceanography	UCLA
1958	Robert Bieri	Oceanography	UCLA
	John Stratlii Bradshaw	Oceanography	UCLA
	Edward Brinton	Oceanography	UCLA
	David Ely Contois	Microbiology	UCLA
	Eugene Francis Corcoran	Oceanography	UCLA
	John Lyman	Oceanography	UCLA
	Robert Walter Rex	Oceanography	UCLA
	Takayasu Uchio	Oceanography	UCLA
1959	Joseph Ross Curray	Oceanography	UCLA
	Francis Joseph Howard	Oceanography	UCLA
	John Atkinson Knauss	Oceanography	UCLA
	Arthur Eugene Maxwell	Oceanography	UCLA
	Kenneth Stafford Norris	Zoology	UCLA
	George Alfred Shumway, Jr.	Oceanography	UCLA
1960	Daniel Eddins Andrews, Jr.	Physics	UCLA
	Theodore Klock Chamberlain	Oceanography	UCLA
	Alfred Wallace Ebeling	Zoology	UCLA
	Robert Joseph Hurley	Oceanography	UCLA
	Richard Pierre Von Herzen	Oceanography	UCLA
1961	Bradford Albert Becken	Physics	UCLA
	Raymond Joseph Ghelardi	Oceanography	UCSD
	John Arthur McGowan	Oceanography	UCSD
	Dale Curtiss Krause	Oceanography	UCSD
	Robert Arvid Rasmussen	Physics	UCLA
	Peter Montague Williams	Oceanography	UCLA
1962	Carl Milton Boyd, Jr.	Marine Biology	UCSD
	William Dixon Clarke	Oceanography	UCSD
	James Thomas Enright	Zoology	UCLA
	Robert Renninger Lankford	Oceanography	UCSD
1963	David Regier Schink	Oceanography	UCSD
	Robert Irwin Clutter	Oceanography	UCSD

DATE	NAME	FIELD	WHERE CONFERRED
1964	Harold Berkson	Marine Biology	UCSD
	Stephen Edward Calvert	Oceanography	UCSD
	Robert Floyd Dill	Oceanography	UCSD
	George Wilbur Harvey	Marine Biology	UCSD
	Gaylord Riggs Miller	Oceanography	UCSD
	John Glynn Pierce	Physics	Revelle College UCSD
	Richard Porter Phillips	Earth Science	Revelle College UCSD
	Michael Edward Q. Pilson	Marine Biology	UCSD
	Peter Berkley Taylor	Marine Biology	UCSD
1965	Bruno D'Angeljan-Chatillon	Oceanography	UCSD
	John William Caperon	Oceanography	UCSD
	David James Chapman	Marine Biology	UCSD
	Lewis Hart Cohen	Earth Science	Revelle College UCSD
	Kent Carl Condie	Earth Science	Revelle College UCSD
	Calvin Crowell Daetwyler	Oceanography	UCSD
	Jack Roland Dymond	Oceanography	UCSD
	Richard Fiske Ford	Oceanography	UCSD
	Theodore Dean Foster	Physics	UCSD
	Brent Sherman Gallagher	Oceanography	UCSD
	Ronald John Gibbs	Oceanography	UCSD
	Abraham Golik	Oceanography	UCSD
	William Robert Holland	Oceanography	UCSD
	James Sargent Kittredge	Oceanography	UCSD
	Bui-Thi Lang	Marine Biology	UCSD
	Robert Wolcott Lewis	Marine Biology	UCSD
	Glenn Straghan Mackenzie	Earth Science	Revelle College UCSD
	Garth Ivor Murphy	Oceanography	UCSD
	George Vincent Pickwell	Marine Biology	UCSD
	David Alexander Ross	Oceanography	UCSD
	Russell Lewis Snyder	Oceanography	UCSD
	Alan Michael Stueber	Earth Science	Revelle College UCSD
	Bruce Alan Taft	Oceanography	UCSD
	Robert Wayne Thompson	Oceanography	UCSD
	Hans Herbert Veeh	Oceanography	UCSD
1966	Abner Blackman	Oceanography	UCSD
	William Fisher Busby	Marine Biology	UCSD
	George Frederick Crozier	Marine Biology	UCSD
	Kern Ellsworth Kenyon	Oceanography	UCSD
	Stanley Arba Kling	Oceanography	UCSD
	Jimmy Carl Larsen	Oceanography	UCSD
	Paul Pushkar	Earth Science	Revelle College UCSD
	Erk Reimnitz	Oceanography	UCSD
	Helmuth Sandstrom	Oceanography	UCSD

APPENDIX I

Ocean-going Ships of the Scripps Institution of Oceanography—Today

Name:	Horizon	Argo	Alexander Agassiz	Oconostota
Type:	Tug	Rescue & Salvage	Light Freight	Tug
Hull:	Steel	Steel	Steel	Steel
Year Built:	1944	1944	1944	1944
Year Acquired by SIO:	1948	1959	1961	1962
From Whom Acquired:	U. S. Navy	U. S. Navy	State Educ. Agency for Surplus Property	U. S. Navy
Owner:	Univ. of Calif.	U. S. Navy	Univ. of Calif.	U. S. Navy
Length:	143'	213'	180'	102'
Beam:	33'	40'	32'	25'
Draft:	13'6"	39'6"	10'	10'
Displacement:	900 Tons (Full)	2,079 Tons (Full)	825 Tons (Full)	206 Tons (F
Cruising Speed:	11½	13	11	12
Maximum Speed:	12½	14	12	12
Minimum Speed:	½	½	3	½
Range (Miles):	6,800	8,000	7,700	6,000
Endurance (Days):	48	60	27	25
Crew:	19	32	17	8
Scientific Party:	16	24	14	6

n B. Scripps	Thomas Washington	Alpha Helix	T-441
-Shore Supply	Oceanographic Research	Oceanographic Research	Cargo & Passenger
el	Steel	Steel	Steel
4-1965	1965	1965-1966	1953
5	1965	1966	1955
ntzler Boat & Barge Co. (Leased)	U. S. Navy	Nat. Science Found.	U. S. Navy
ntzler Boat & arge Co.	U. S. Navy	Univ. of Calif.	U. S. Navy
	209′	133′	65′
	40′	31′	18′
	14′	10′5½″	6′
Tons (Full)	1,362 Tons (Full)	512 Tons (Full)	99 Tons (Full)
	11	11	10½
	12	12	11
	½	3	3
o	8,000	6,200	1,830
	48	24	5
	25	12	
	16	10	9 including crew

BIBLIOGRAPHY

PRIMARY SOURCES

MANUSCRIPTS, REPORTS AND PERSONAL MEMOIRS

IN SCRIPPS INSTITUTION OF OCEANOGRAPHY ARCHIVES

Fortune, Carolyn Vaughan. *Private scrapbook* (re father, T. Wayland Vaughan and family, now in the possession of the family.)

Hinton, Sam. *History of the Scripps Institution of Oceanography, 1892-1951.* Mimeographed manuscript of chronological history. 4 p.

Marine Biological Station. Wm. E. Ritter's report to the President of the University, July 1, 1910, reprinted in biennial report of the President of the University on behalf of the Regents to His Excellency the Governor of the State, 1908-10.

Marine Biological Association of San Diego. *Corporate records,* May 3, 1904-Dec. 7, 1908. 39 p.

Marine Biological Association of San Diego. *By-laws and minutes,* Aug. 2, 1903-Dec. 2, 1911. (Handwritten)

Marine Biological Association of San Diego. *Account book,* May 6, 1903-March, 1913.

Marine Biological Association of San Diego. *Unpublished correspondence,* 1903-1912. (Letters of W. E. Ritter, Fred Baker, Charles Kofoid, Julius Wangenheim, E. W. Scripps, Miss Ellen B. Scripps, President Wheeler and others.)

McEwen, George F. *The Scripps Institution,* Dec. 1921. Manuscript, 8 p.

Miller, H. Loye. *Gulf of California cruise 1939 "E. W. Scripps."* Manuscript, 41 p. illus.

National Academy of Sciences, Committee on Oceanography. Letters and reports of this committee preserved by committee member, T. Wayland Vaughan, 1927-31.

Ragan, Ruth. A collection of book reviews, criticisms, etc., of the book *The Oceans* by Harald U. Sverdrup, Martin W. Johnson, Richard H. Fleming. Collected by Ruth Ragan, 1942-46. Bound manuscript. 75 p. illus.

Raitt, Helen H. *Give us room,* Two radio talks, Dec. 17, 1961, and Jan. 28, 1962, Radio KGB, San Diego. Mimeographed manuscript, 12 p. (a short account of the early days.)

Ritter, Mary Bennett. *Diaries,* 1919-37. 4 v.

Ritter, William E. *A popular lecture to the citizens of La Jolla,* July, 1907. Unpublished speech. 10 p.

Scripps, Edward W. Unpublished disquisitions and letters.

Scripps Institution for Biological Research. *By-laws and minutes,* July, 1912-Sept. 17, 1918.

Scripps Institution for Biological Research. *Annual report of the Director of Scripps Institution for Biological Research to the President of the University, July 1, 1912,* printed in Biennial report of the President of the University on behalf of the Regents to His Excellency the Governor of the State, 1910-12.

Scripps Institution for Biological Research. *Annual report of the Director of Scripps Institution for Biological Research to the President of the University of California, 1912-1924.* Reprinted from the Annual Report of the President of the University, 1912-24.

Scripps Institution for Biological Research. *Unpublished correspondence,* 1912-26. Letters of W. E. Ritter, Fred Baker, F. B. Sumner, W. E. Allen, W. C. Crandall, George McEwen, J. C. Harper, E. W. Scripps, Miss Ellen Scripps, T. Wayland Vaughan, President Wheeler and others.

Scripps Institution for Biological Research, Reprints regarding the Institution from the *University Register,* 1917-19, 1923-24.

Scripps Institution of Oceanography. *Photographic scrapbooks and photographs,* 1902-

Scripps Institution of Oceanography. Announcements from *University of California Register,* 1926-35.

Scripps Institution of Oceanography. *Annual report of the Director of Scripps Institution of Oceanography to the President of the University, 1926-30.* Printed in annual report of the President 1926-30.

Scripps Institution of Oceanography. *Annual report from the Director of Scripps Institution of Oceanography to the President of the University of California,* 1930-46.

Scripps Institution of Oceanography. *Unpublished correspondence,* 1926-52.

Scripps Institution of Oceanography. *General catalogue of the University of California, Scripps Institution of Oceanography,* 1934-38.

Scripps Institution of Oceanography. *History in the news, 1919-1960.* Thirteen bound volumes of newspaper clippings and typed publicity releases.

Scripps Institution of Oceanography. Series of radio talks on Scripps Institution of Oceanography, 1933-34, 1935.

Scripps Institution of Oceanography. *University Register from the Scripps Institution of Oceanography announcements file, 1948-51.*

Scripps Institution of Oceanography. *Publicity releases,* 1948-50.

Scripps Institution of Oceanography. *Annual reports of the business office of Scripps Institution of Oceanography,* 1946-48.

Scripps Institution of Oceanography. *"E. W. Scripps" ship file,* 1944-47, 1948-49.

Scripps Institution of Oceanography. *Document files.*

Scripps Institution of Oceanography. *Announcement University of California, San Diego, Scripps Institution of Oceanography,* 1964.

Spiess, Fred N. *Scripps and the world oceans.* Faculty lecture, Sumner auditorium, May 11, 1965. Manuscript. 14 p.

Sumner, Francis B. *The Scripps Institution,* 1923, Manuscript. 11 p.

Sumner, Francis B. *Suggestions respecting the needs of the Scripps Institution,* 1915, Manuscript, 10 p.

Sumner, Francis B. *The life and times of Francis Bertody Sumner by himself,* April 4, 1944. Manuscript. 6 p.

Sverdrup, Harald U. *Informal autobiography and supplement.* La Jolla, Feb. 6, 1948. Manuscript. 12 p.

Sverdrup, H. U. and Walter H. Munk. *Wind, waves and swell; a basic theory for forecasting.* Wave Report no. 1, 1943.

University of California. *Summer sessions at San Pedro, 1900-02.* Letters, financial records, announcements, etc.

Vaughan, T. Wayland. *Geological notebooks and scrapbooks.* 7 v.

BOOKS, PAMPHLETS AND ARTICLES

Agassiz, Alexander. *Letters and recollections of Alexander Agassiz, with a sketch of his life and work.* Edited by G. R. Agassiz. Houghton, Mifflin, Boston, 1913.

Bernard, Robert J. "Ellen Browning Scripps; woman of vision," *California Scripps College Bulletin,* Oct. 14, 1926.

Baker, Fred. "Dr. Ritter and the founding of the Scripps Institution of Oceanography" at the presentation and acceptance of a portrait of Dr. William Emerson Ritter, first Director of the Scripps Institution presented by Miss Ellen Browning Scripps to the Scripps Institution of Oceanography, University of California. Scripps Institution of Oceanography *Bulletin* (non-technical) 15 (Jan. 28, 1928) 5-13.

Bigelow, Henry B. *Oceanography; its scope, problems and economic importance.* Houghton, Mifflin, Boston, 1931.

Bigelow, Henry B. "Presentation of the Agassiz Medal to Dr. Thomas Wayland Vaughan," *Science,* 83 (May 22, 1936) 474-475.

Britt, Albert. *Ellen Browning Scripps, journalist and idealist,* printed for Scripps College, University Press, Oxford, 1960.

California. University. Division of War Research. *Completion report* made to the Chief of the Bureau of Ships, Navy Department, covering operations of the University of California Division of War Research at the U.S. Navy Electronics Laboratory, San Diego, California, under Contract NObs-2074 (formerly DEMsr-30) from 26 April 1941 to June 30, 1946. Unclassified per SECDEF memo 8-2-60.

California. University. Los Angeles. Graduate Division. *25th Anniversary of doctorate awards at UCLA.* Los Angeles, 1964.

Cochran, Negley D. *E. W. Scripps.* Harcourt, Brace, New York, 1933.

Coe, Wesley R. "The Scripps Institution of the University of California," *American journal of science,* 14 (Sept. 1927) 237-239.

Coker, R. E. *This great and wide sea; an introduction to oceanography and marine biology.* Univ. of North Carolina Press, Chapel Hill, N. C., 1947.

Complete Collected Works of William E. Ritter, T. Wayland Vaughan, Harald U. Sverdrup, Francis B. Sumner, Ellis Michael, Winfred E. Allen, George E. McEwen, Erik G. Moberg.

Dickson, Edward A. *University of California at Los Angeles; its origin and formative years.* Friends of the UCLA Library, Los Angeles, 1955.

Fox, Denis L. "Francis Bertody Sumner," *Year book of the American Philosophical Society* (1945) 416-420.

Gardner, Gilson. *Lusty Scripps; the life E. W. Scripps (1854-1926)* Vanguard Press, New York, 1932. Appendix contains last Will and Testament of Edward W. Scripps.

Gates. Charles M. *The first century at the University of Washington, 1861-1961.* University of Washington Press. Seattle, 1961.

Hall, Mary Harrington. "Revelle," *San Diego and point magazine,* 13 (May 1961) 40+.

Hall, Mary Harrington. "UCSD," *San Diego and point magazine,* 16 (April 1964) 50+.

Hall, Mary Harrington. "Inside UCSD, part II: Scripps wherever the four winds blew," *San Diego and point magazine,* 16 (May 1964) 55+.

Hamilton, Edward L. "Sunken islands of the mid-Pacific mountains," Geological Society of America, *Memoir,* 64 (March 10, 1956) 1-97.

Harper, Jacob C. *Ellen Browning Scripps.* Privately published, La Jolla, 1936.

Herdman, W. A. *Founders of oceanography and their work.* E. Arnold, London, 1923.

Hill, Maurice N., general editor, and others. *The Sea,* Interscience Publishers, New York, 1962-63. 3 v.

Johnson, Myrtle Elizabeth and Harry James Snook. *Seashore animals of the Pacific coast.* Macmillan, New York, 1927.

Kofoid, Charles A. "The San Diego Biological Laboratory," *University of California chronicle,* 9 (1907) 61-65.

Lillie, Frank R. *The Woods Hole Marine Biological Laboratory.* University of Chicago Press, Chicago, 1944.

McCabe, Charles R. *Damned old crank.* Harper, New York, 1951.

Martin, James R. *The University of California in Los Angeles.* N.p., 1925.

McEwen, George E. "The University and the Pacific, the story of Scripps Institution," *The California monthly,* March, 1937, 4 p. Also in: Scripps Institution of Oceanography *Contributions,* v. 34, no. 10.

National Academy of Sciences—National Research Council. Committee on Oceanography. *Oceanography 1960 to 1970,* Section 11: History of oceanography. Washington, D. C., 1962.

"Open Forum strikes fire Monday meetings near row," *La Jolla Journal,* Aug. 3, 1917.

Phifer, Lyman D. and Margaret W. Phifer. "The Puget Sound Biological Station," reprint from *The Biologist,* 12 (Sept. 1930) 13 p.

Raitt, Helen. *Exploring the deep pacific.* W. W. Norton, New York, 1956.

Randolph, Howard S. *La Jolla year by year.* Library Association of La Jolla, 1955.

Revelle, Roger and Walter Munk. "Harald Ulrik Sverdrup; an appreciation" Journal of marine research, 7 (Nov. 15, 1948) 127-131. Sverdrup sixtieth anniversary volume.

Ritter, Mary B. *More than gold in California.* Professional Press, Berkeley, 1933.

Ritter, William E. "The Harriman Alaskan expedition," *University of California chronicle,* 2 (Aug. 1899) 225-232. Also in: Ritter's Collected works, v. 2, no. 8.

Ritter, William E. "Marine biology and the marine laboratory at San Pedro," *The University of California chronicle,* 5 (1902) 222-230.

Ritter, William E. "A summer's dredging on the coast of Southern California," *Science,* 15 (Jan. 10, 1902) 55-65.

Ritter, William E. "Report as Director of the Marine Biological Laboratory at Coronado to the Laboratory Committee of the Chamber of Commerce of San Diego," *The San Diego Union*, (Aug. 1, 1903).

Ritter, William E. "A permanent school of Biological Research at San Diego," *The San Diego Union*, (Sept. 25, 1903).

Ritter, William E. "Preliminary report on the marine biological survey work carried on by the Zoological Department of the University of California at San Diego," *Science* (Sept. 18, 1905) 360-366.

Ritter, William E. "A general statement of the ideas and the present aims and status of the Marine Biological Association of San Diego," *University of California publications in zoology*, 2 (1905) 1-17.

Ritter, William E. "Marine Biological Association of San Diego," *Science*, 26 (Sept. 20, 1907) 386-388.

Ritter, William E. "The scientific work of the San Diego Marine Biological Station during the year 1908," *Science*, 28 (Sept. 1908) 324-333.

Ritter, William E. *The Marine Biological Station of San Diego; a sketch of its history and purposes.* Frye and Smith, San Diego, 1910.

Ritter, William E. "Work of the Marine Biological Station of San Diego during the summer of 1911," *Science*, 34 (Oct. 13, 1911) 480-483.

Ritter, William E. "The Marine Biological Station of San Diego; its history, present conditions, achievements, and aims," *University of California publications in zoology*, 9 (March 9, 1912) 137-248.

Ritter, William E. *War, science and civilization*, French and Company, Boston, 1915.

Ritter, William E. "The biological laboratories of the Pacific coast," *Popular science monthly*, (March 1915) 223-232. Also in: Scripps Institution of Oceanography contributions, v. 11, no. 21.

Ritter, William E. "What the Scripps Institution is trying to do," Scripps Institution for Biological Research, *Bulletin*, 1 (Dec. 30, 1916) 19-24.

Ritter, William E. *An organismal theory of consciousness.* R. E. Badger, Boston, 1919.

Ritter, William E. *The unity of the organism or the organismal conception of life.* R. E. Badger, Boston, 1919. 2 v.

Ritter, William E. "Ellis L. Michael and his scientific work," *Ecology*, 2 (Jan. 1921) 70-72.

Ritter, William E. and Edna W. Bailey. *The natural history of our conduct.* Harcourt, Brace & Co., New York, 1927.

Ritter, William E. "The relation of E. W. Scripps to science." *Science*, 65 (March 25, 1927) 291-292.

Ritter, William E. "The man, E. W. Scripps," Scripps College, Claremont, California, *Bulletin* (Sept. 30, 1929) 1-14.

Ritter, William E. "The name, Scripps Institution of Oceanography," *Science*, 84 (July 24, 1936) 83.

Ritter, William E. *The California Woodpecker and I: a study in comparative Zoology.* University of California Press, Berkeley, 1938.

Ritter, William E. "Dr. Fred Baker," *Science*, 88 (July 15, 1938) 48-49.

Ritter, William E. *Charles Darwin and the golden rule*. Compiled and edited by Edna Watson Bailey. Storm Publishers, New York, 1954. The introd. is by Bailey, and book contains a complete bibliography of W. E. Ritter's works.

Sargent, Marston C. "The Scripps Institution of Oceanography," *Naval research reviews* (Dec. 1965) 1-11.

Scripps, Edward W. *I protest*, edited by Oliver Knight. University of Wisconsin Press, 1966.

Scripps Institution for Biological Research. "Dedicatory addresses by David Starr Jordan, Daniel Trembly Macdougal, George Howard Parker, William Emerson Ritter," *Bulletin of the Scripps Institution for Biological Research*, No. 1 (Dec. 30, 1916).

Scripps Institution of Oceanography. *Contributions*. 1st series, 1892-1937, 2nd series, 1938-.

Scripps Institution of Oceanography. *Bulletins*. 1st series, 1-16 (1916-1930), 2nd series 1-8 (1927-1964.)

Sumner, Francis B. "William Emerson Ritter: Naturalist and Philosopher," *Science* 99 (April 28, 1944) 335-338.

Sumner, Francis B. *The life history of an American naturalist*. J. Cattell Press, Lancaster, Pa., 1945.

Sverdrup, Harald U. "The work at the Scripps Institution of Oceanography," *Collecting net*, 12 (July, 1937) 57.

Sverdrup, Harald U. and R. H. Fleming, "The waters off the coast of southern California, March to July, 1937," Scripps Institution of Oceanography, *Bulletin*, 4, no. 10 (1941) 261-378.

Sverdrup, Harald U. *The Gulf of California; preliminary discussion of the cruise of the "E. W. Scripps" in February and March, 1939*. Pacific Science Congress, Calif. 6th, 1939. *Proceedings*, v. 3, p. 161-166.

Sverdrup, Harald U. *Activities of the Scripps Institution of Oceanography, La Jolla, California*, Pacific Science Congress, Calif. 6th, 1939. *Proceedings* v. 3, p. 114-123.

Sverdrup, Harald U. "Response of the medallist; presentation of the Agassiz Medal to H. U. Sverdrup," *Science* 90 (July 14, 1939) 24-27.

Sverdrup, Harald U., Martin W. Johnson, and Richard H. Fleming, *The oceans: their physics, chemistry and general biology*. Prentice-Hall, New York, 1942.

Sverdrup, Harald U. *Oceanography for meteorologists*. Prentice-Hall, New York, 1942.

Sverdrup, H. U. and W. H. Munk. *Wind, sea, and swell; theory of relations for forecasting*. U. S. Hydrogr. Off., *Technical report* no. 1; H. O. Publication, no. 601, 1947. 44 p.

Torrey, Harry B. "An unusual occurrence of Dinoflagellata on the California coast," *American Naturalist*, 36 (1902) 187-192.

Vaughan, T. Wayland. "Oceanographic investigations of the Scripps Institution for Biological Research of the University of California," *Science*, 23 (Jan. 1, 1926) 8-10.

Vaughan, T. Wayland. "Biological research at the Scripps Institution of Oceanography," *Science*, 68 (March 19, 1926) 297.

Vaughan, T. Wayland. "Australiaut plants for ornamental purposes in California," *La Jolla flower journal*, (Jan. 1928) 5-6.

Vaughan, T. Wayland. "Outstanding problems of the oceanography of the Pacific," *Scientific monthly*, 34 (Feb. 1932) 128-146.

Vaughan, T. Wayland. "Research facilities at the Scripps Institution of Oceanography," *The Collecting net*, 8 (July 1933) 2-7.

Vaughan, T. Wayland. "Response of the medallist," *Science*, 83 (May 22, 1936) 475-477.

Vaughan, T. Wayland and others. *International aspects of oceanography*. National Academy of Sciences, Washington, D. C., 1937.

Vaughan, T. Wayland. Presentation of the Agassiz Medal to Harald Ulrik Sverdrup. *Science*, 90 (July 14, 1939) 24-27.

Vetter, Richard C., comp. *An international directory of oceanographers*. 4th ed. National Academy of Science-National Research Council, Washington, D. C., 1964.

Wangenheim, Julius. "Julius Wangenheim, an autobiography," *California Historical Society Quarterly*, a series of articles beginning with v.35 (June, 1956.)

Whitaker, Thomas and others. *Torrey Pines State Reserve*. Drawings by Margaret Eddy Fleming. The Torrey Pines Association, La Jolla, 1964.

Whitney, Frederick C. "Sverdrup of Scripps," *Joe Morgan's La Jollan*, 1 (Dec. 4, 1946) 18-19+.

Wüst, Georg. "The major deep-sea expeditions and research vessels, 1873-1960," *Progress in oceanography*, Pergamon Press, London, 1964. v.2, p.3-52.

ZoBell, Claude. "Biological research at the Scripps Institution of Oceanography," *The Collecting net*, 11 (Aug. 1, 1936) 1-5.

INDEX

Abraham Lincoln (ship), 165
Acton and Co., 35, 53
Adler-Mereschkowsky, W. C., 9
agar, 142
Agassiz, Alexander, 36
Agassiz's South Sea Expedition, 1904-05, 36
Alaska, 6
albacore, long-finned (tuna), 90
Albatross (ship), 26, 86
Aleutian Islands, 114, 117
Alexander Agassiz (ship), 50, 53, 59, 61,
 68-69, 84, 91, 112, 162, 200
Allen, B. M., 61
Allen, Winfred E., 83, 139, 164, 187-189
Alligator Head, La Jolla, 30, 41-42, 45
Alpha Helix (ship), xviii, 154, 200
Alvarino de Leira, Angeles, 197
American Association for the Advance-
 ment of Science (AAAS), 93-94
American Geophysical Union (AGU), 143
American Petroleum Institute (API), 139
Anderson, D. Q., 188
Anderson, Ernest Robert, 194
Anderson, Victor C., 191, 194
Andrews, Daniel E., Jr., 191, 195
Antarctic, 119
Anza-Borrego Desert State Park, 163
Apia, Samoa, 113
apparatus, see instruments and apparatus
appendiculariae, 83
Applied Oceanography Group
 (AOG), 153-154
aquarium-museum, 9, 21, 35, 42, 49,
 72-73, 78, 148, 154
Arctic, 119
Argo (ship), 154, 156, 200
Armstrong, Ursel S., 188
Army Air Corps, 140
"Around the world in 80 days," 166
Arthur, David Kilgore, 195
Arthur, Robert S., 165,194
ascidian, 74
Assembly in Science, 73
Atlantic Ocean, 109
Atlantis (ship), 110, 144
atom bomb, 142
Atomic Energy Commission (AEC), 153
Atwood, Katherine, 190
auction, Pueblo Lot 1298, 48
Asia, 37-38, 41-42
Australia, 98
Australian Botanical Gardens, 105

Babcock, E. S., 12, 14-15, 23, 158
Backus, George E., 197
Bahamas, 82
Bailey, Edna Watson, 160

Baja California, 124, 130, 132
Baker, Charlotte, 4, 13, 98, 157
Baker, Fred, 3, 9-10, 12-15, 17, 19-21, 25,
 27-28, 30, 35-36, 39-41, 45-46, 65, 68,
 98, 112, 157-159, 188
Baker, Molly, 158
Ball, Henry, 121
Bancroft, Frank, 8
Barnhart, Percy S., 72, 74, 78, 93,
 148, 161, 189
Barnhart, Mrs. Percy S., 77, 187-188
Barr, Edward S., 167
Barrows, A. L., 99, 186
Baruch, Jacob, 10
bathythermograph observations
 collection, 155
Batzler, William, 167
Becken, Bradford A., 196
Beers, John R., 197
Bennett, Mary, 4
Benson, Andrew A., 186
Berkson, Harold, 196
Bermuda Biological Station, 109-110
Berner, Leo D., Jr., 195
Berry, S. Stillman, 83
Bieri, Robert, 195
Bigelow, Henry B., 116, 119
Bigelow report, 109, 164
Bikini Atoll, 142-143
"Biological Grade," 77, 160, 163
"Biology Beach," 76
Black, Jeremiah, 167
Blackburn, Maurice, 197
Blackman, Abner, 197
Blind Goby, 4
Block, Barry, 197
Boden, Brian B., 194
bottom deposits, see sedimentation,
 cores, and bottom deposits
bottom fauna, 16
bottom topography, 133, 138-139
Bovard, J. F., 16
Bowditch (ship), 142-143
Bowers, George M., 11
Bowie, William, 163
Bowman, Thomas E., 191, 195
Boyd, Carl M., 196
Bradner, Hugh, 197
Bradshaw, John S., 195
Brandt, R. P., 187
Branner, J. C., 13
Brayton, George E., 167
Brinton, Edward, 195, 197
Britt, Albert, 158
Broderick, Mr., 161
Brown University, 148
Burbridge, H. C., 59, 61, 186

Bureau of Soils, *see* U. S. Dept.
  of Agriculture
Burnam, F. R., 157-158
Burt, Wayne, 165, 194
Busby, William F., 197
Bushnell (ship), 117
Butcher, William Sherman, 194
Butler, J. T., 48, 181

Cabral, Manuel, 15-16, 26-27, 39
Caldwell, Douglas R., 197
California Institute of Technology, 134
California State Game & Fish
  Commission, 61, 90, 142
California woodpecker, 162
Calvert, Stephen E., 196
Cameron, William Maxwell, 194
Camp Callan, 146
Camp Elliot, 166
Campbell, W. W., 97-100, 106, 163, 187-188
Cape San Lucas, Baja Calif., 132
Caperon, John W., 196
Carbon-14 laboratory, 155
Carey, Mrs., 41
Caribbean, 102
Carlson, D. A., 16
Carlson, Deane R., 167
Carlucci, Angelo F., 197
Carnegie (ship), 112-113
Carnegie Expedition in the Pacific, 119
Carnegie Institution of Washington,
  D. C., 62, 74, 112-113, 163-164
Carritt, Dayton E. ("David"), 148, 189
Carsola, Alfred J., 194
Catalina Island, *see* Santa Catalina Island
cattle problems, 57
Cedros Island, Baja Calif., 130, 132
chaetognatha, 60, 81
Chamberlain, Theodore K., 195
Chambers, Stanley W., 188-189, 191
Channel Islands, 112, 130
Chapman, David J., 196
Chester W. Nimitz Marine Facility, 154
Child, C. M., 59
Christensen, Ralph, 165
Chukchi Indians, *see* Reindeer Chukchi
Cincinnati, O., 57
Clarke, William D., 196
Clayton, W. E., 158
Clutter, Robert I., 196
Cochran, E. L., 145, 166
Cochrane, John D., 191
Coe, Wesley R., 191
coelenterata, 15
Cohen, Lewis H., 196
Collins, H. H., 187
Colorado River, 133-134

Columbia University, 38, 166
Committee of Pacific Investigation,
  see National Research Council
Committee on Conservation of Marine
  Life of the Pacific, *see* AAAS
Committee on Oceanography,
  see National Academy of Sciences
conchology, 13
Condie, Kent C., 196
Congress, 11
Conklin, E. G., 163
Contois, David E., 195
copepoda, 16, 60, 82
corals and coral reefs, 97
Corcoran, Eugene F., 195
cores & coring, *see* sedimentation,
  cores and bottom deposits
Corley, James, 166
Coronado, Calif., 14-16, 19, 26-27, 36, 51
Coronado Beach Co., 13, 28, 158
Coronado boathouse, 13-14, 16, 23, 132
Cortes Bank, 51
Cosby, Scott, 167
Costa Rica, 117
Council of Defense of California, 91
Cox, Charles S., 195
Crandall, Wesley Clarence, 61, 69, 71,
  75-76, 88-91, 93-101, 160, 162, 286-287
Crandall, Mrs. Wesley Clarence, 160, 162
Crane, Sheldon C., 189, 194
Crest (ship), 147
Crozier, George F., 197
ctenophora, 83
Cummings, N. W., 85
Cupp, Easter E., 188
Curray, Joseph R., 195
current meter, 135
Cuyamaca State Park, 163

Daetwyler, Calvin C., 196
Dahl, John, 59
D'Angeljan-Chatillon, Bruno, 196
Daniel, J. Frank, 186-187
data gathering, continuity in, 31
Davis, B. M., 16, 27
Davis, C. C., 165, 194
Davis, Sallie May, 165
deep scattering layer, 139, 165
Deep Sea Drilling Project, xviii
Del Mar, Calif., 42, 46, 48
densities, 82
Denver, Colorado, 89
Desert Museum, Palm Springs, Calif., 148
Detroit, Mich., 19
Detroit Tribune (newspaper), 18
Deutsch, Monroe E., 120, 164
diatoms, 83

Lorenzen, Carl, 197
Los Angeles, Calif., 7, 24, 42, 49, 77
Los Angeles Normal School, 16
Los Angeles Steamship Co., 107
Louderback, George D., 119-120, 164
Ludington, W. F., 43
Ludwick, John C., Jr., 194
Lura (ship), 15, 26
Lyman, John, 165, 195

MacDougal, D. T., 74
MacKenzie, Glenn S., 196
MacMullen, James, 21, 29
Maler, Obie, 163
manta rays, 133
Mao, Han-Lee, 194
Marine Biological Association of
    San Diego, 20, 23-24, 46-48, 53-54,
    60-62, 64, 69, 101
Marine Biological Laboratory, Woods
    Hole, Mass., 5, 110, 116, 157, 163
Marine Biological Station,
    Nanaimo, B. C., 117
marine invertebrate collection, 7, 155
Marine Laboratory Committee,
    see San Diego Chamber of Commerce
Marine Life Research Group,
    (MLRG), 147, 153
marine microbiology, 107, 129
Marine Physical Laboratory,
    (MPL), 145, 150, 153-154
marine resources, 92-93
Mark, E. L., 38-43
Marshall Islands, 150
Marston, George W., 20, 158
Mason, Max, 110
mass spectrographs, 155
Maud (ship), 119, 149
Maxwell, Arthur E., 167, 195
McAlister, Edward D., 197
McGowan, John A., 196-197
McIlvaine, Carl E., 197
McLeish, William L., 197
McLellan, Hugh J., 195
McEwen, George F., 51, 59, 61, 82-83,
    85-86, 116, 120, 129, 186-190
McEwen, Mrs. George F., 160
McHugh, John L., 191, 194
McKinley, James W., 24, 38
McKitrick, Ruth, 189
McMillan, D. J., 167
McRae, 19
Menard, H. W., 167
Mecerau Bridge and Construction Co., 71
Merriam, J. C., 113, 163
Merritt, Ralph P., 67-69, 71, 160

meteorological research,
    see weather forecasting
Miami University, Oxford, Ohio, 102
mice, see Peromyscus
Michael, Ellis L., 59-60, 81, 84, 101, 159,
    186-187
Midpac, see Operation Mid-Pacific
Mid-Pacific Mountains, 150
Miles, John W., 197
Miller, Gaylord R., 196
Miller, H. Loye, 132
Miller, Julian K., 197
Miramar Ranch, 19, 24, 36, 39
Mission Bay Bridge, 86
Moberg, Eric G., 85, 112, 117-118,
    120, 123, 132, 187-188
mollusca, 132
Monk, C. R., 165, 194
Monrovia, Liberia, 102
Morita, Richard Y., 167, 195
Mullin, Michael M., 197
Munk, Walter H., 134, 140, 143, 149,
    161, 166, 189-190, 194, 197
murarium or "mouse house," 87, 89
Murphy, Garth I., 196
museum, see aquarium-museum
Museum of Comparative Zoology,
    see Harvard University

NEL, see Navy Electronics Laboratory
Nasu, Noriyuki, 195
National Academy of Sciences,
    93-94, 108-110, 117, 163-164
National Defense Research
    Council, 137, 144
National Research Council, 93-94, 197
National Science Foundation (NSF), 153
Nautilus (ship), 119
Naval Postgraduate School,
    Monterey, Calif., 165
Navy Electronics Laboratory,
    144-146, 150, 154
Navy Radio and Sound
    Laboratory, 135, 165
net hauls, 82
New Mexico, 13
Newkirk, J. N., 19, 158
Nierenberg, William A., xvii-xix,
    152, 186, 191
Norris, Dr., 95
Norris, Robert M., 194
Norris, Kenneth S., 195
North, Wheeler J., 194
North Africa, 140-141
Norway, 119, 135-136, 140, 149-150
Norwegian Polar Institute, 149
Novia Del Mar (ship), 123-124